THE MEXICAN CENTAUR :

an intimate biography
of
PANCHO VILLA

OREN ARNOLD

PORTALS PRESS

FOREWORD

This is a biography. Yet we are fortunate that its author avoided what is commonly called "biographical style." In presenting so fabulous a character as Pancho Villa, it would have been a literary breach of faith merely to *tell* about him; far better to reenact his life, unfolding it incident by incident, adventure by adventure, scene by dramatic scene, right on through to its terrifying finale. The story of Pancho could not possibly have had proper scope in any but this technique normally reserved for fiction.

Such does not lessen the value of the work; rather is it enhanced. There have been other books on Pancho Villa and—sad to say—most have made rather dull reading. Their dedicated authors have labored the military details and the immensely complicated politics of his period, or have gone to the other extreme and presented an unrealistic shoot-em-up type of report, completely unauthentic.

In *The Mexican Centaur,* by contrast, we live with the hero. We walk with, and worry with, and suffer with, the boy Doroteo. In closest rapport, we soon break away from his childhood and go racing hell-for-leather beside the young zealot, inspiring the peons and challenging oppressors. When inevitable violence arises, we the readers are *there!* We are not reading about it, we are sharing the action, and if our eyes are widened and we don't sleep well that evening, we at least enjoy the great saga of Mexico. Every mood—and there are many softer ones, many with comic relief—somehow permeates our being. Such is the magic of skillful writing.

Mr. Arnold began his research into the Villista epic in 1925 at El Paso, Texas, and as opportunity presented has gone deep into the Latin land, living with and gaining the confidence of men who rode with Pancho, visiting the women who married him and the women who should have married him, and talking with his endless children. He lifted Pancho's personal swords, tried on his uniforms (which were too large), and sat in his chairs. He hefted Pancho's *pistolas* (they were too heavy). He put his finger into holes made in adobe walls by enemy rifle bullets, and touched old scars on wounds suffered by members of the *insurrecto* band. He retraced the trails and relived the excitement so far as possible; he read every document and clipping available, but tossed most out because they were contradictory, or were mere propaganda pro and con. He was striving to get at not the "outlaw" or the "statesman," but the *mucho hombre*, the man! Here, therefore, is the greatest cavalryman that North America ever knew, come alive; a complex and controversial human being, whose leadership exceeded that of any other person produced by our western world.

Mr. Arnold has published some eighty books. *Writer's digest* has referred to him as "the dean of western American authors." This true narrative of Pancho Villa strengthens that appraisal.

JULY 1979   ALAN D. LE BARON

DEDICATED

with great affection
to my he-man sons-in-law,
who have little in common with Pancho
but who have their own imperfections
and their own glories——

Pat O'Reilly . . . Jerry Detwiler

THE MEXICAN CENTAUR

*"It is better to live six years with Villa
than sixty as a slave."*

1

Doroteo FELT that if the black horse—just this one scarred and slightly sway-backed black gelding—could become his personal property, he would never want for anything else on this earth.

He might want and expect more hereafter, indeed a person had a right to expect more then. The hereafter, the Heavenly home, would have no scrub horses; only the sleek and shiny best ones, the beauties which a boy could love and ride in wild abandon along the golden highways, with everybody smiling and approving. He thought much of the hereafter; it took some of the sting off the now. But the now always came back into his consciousness, and meditating on the black horse helped to bear it.

"Doroteo," he said aloud, there in the dust from the hoofs, "if you *owned* the black horse you could ride!"

He was addressing himself, but he felt no embarrassment at this. He had talked aloud to himself for as long as he could remember, because doing so helped pass the endless hours, the day in and day out loneliness, miles from another human being. Once his mother had gone out there with his forgotten lunch and had caught him. "It is all right," she had said gently, "if you talk to yourself and enjoy it when you are age thirteen this way. It helps the brain to grow."

Actually, the listener was not himself, and Doroteo well knew that. The listener was a very different boy, a bigger one, a happier one, an understanding one deep inside him. Sometimes the two would ride imaginary horses into the nearby mountains, racing up the red rock canyons, having no end of fun.

The inner boy had, among other great blessings, shoes. Doroteo admired shoes. His only real-life garment was an ill-fitting thing of one piece, with two sack pockets which he himself had sewn

1

into it. Shoes meant much. He had seen many of them, some of very fine quality on the land owners and the cattle buyers, when he was allowed near the big ranch houses. His own father, Augustin Arango, had once owned a pair of shoes. These rested even now on a shelf above a door in his widowed mother's hut. It was understood, or at least hoped, that when he, Doroteo, grew big enough for them he might himself put them on. He did not truly expect that. It was too much to hope for; life had a mean habit of dashing one's hopes to pieces. But the inner Doroteo suffered no such. *His* hopes materialized. *He* had shoes. And a warm coat. And abundant food, always. And no sway-backed old black gelding, but a glistening silver stallion.

"If you owned the black horse you could ride," he repeated.

"Yes, I could," he answered himself, aloud.

"Perhaps it wouldn't hurt anything if you rode him anyhow, eh? Just once more. Nobody ever sees you, away out here in the hills. It is far from the corrals, and you have tamed him. And you well know you have a halter hidden in the next mesquite tree!"

Doroteo the outer laughed. He did have a halter hidden. He had made it of cowhide strings, a crude thing, but enough. It was his secret. It even had a lead rope. With this he had tamed the black horse, and had dared to ride a few times. Fear had stopped him, then lately something to defy fear had been welling in him, and the inner Doroteo encouraged this.

"Go on," the inner boy said now. "Ride him. You are not a baby any more. Nobody will see you anyway."

He got out the halter and admired it. He had plaited three quarter-inch thongs and knotted them artfully to make the headstall. A loop under the chin served as a tie ring. A rosette, fashioned of brown, white, and black hair-on-hide, cut into circles of three sizes then joined in the center, was tied to the halter's right side. This was pure ornament, but was important. He had personally cut the thongs and the rosette, with another treasured possession, a pocket knife. This knife had half its bone handle missing and one blade broken off, but the other blade was good. It had been rusted when he found it a year ago, but he had ground off the rust until it shone like Don Felipe's saddle silver. Thus it too was beautiful now, it too helped make life endurable, it was a thing owned.

The sway-backed gelding seemed to welcome him. When

2

Doroteo approached holding the halter, others of the herd moved away. The black lifted his head and waited.

"Ho-o-o-o-o," said Doroteo, soothingly, but with assurance. "You are my horse. We are friends, remember. I have taught you to ride. Is a good horse. Ho-o-o-o-o-o."

Just sounds. Just calm and gentle words which he knew the horse did not understand except by tone. There are two ways to handle horses, he well knew. One is by the lariat with force and vigor, the other is by hand with tenderness and patience.

Doroteo admired both techniques but perforce had only one to use. In scarcely a moment he had the halter tied on and, grasping the mane in his left hand, swung across the gelding's back with his own animal-like grace of motion.

For a second or two both waited poised. Doroteo, not conscience stricken, but stabbed by an eternally present dagger of fear, looked quickly around. Nobody was in sight.

He touched the black gelding's ribs and shot away in a flourish. They ran, just ran, along the gentle slope of the valley pasture there; ran a mile, turned and ran back again. The herd was quietly grazing, unchanged. But Doroteo was changed. Now he was without servility or fear. Now he was astride a servant at his command. Truly, there is something special about a man on a horse. He is a warrior bold, a conqueror, a centaur. Doroteo sensed these things, first the inner boy then the poorly clad and barefoot one. A new dignity sat upon him. An inspiriting something touched his soul.

He swung low, clinging Indian fashion by foot over the back and by hand-hold on the mane, to pick a long stick off the ground. It was a section of dried sotol, the strange cactus-like stalk of Mexico, light and strong. He broke this and retained a section the length of his arm, studied it a moment, boyish eyes shining. This was no stick, no whip for the horse. This was a blade of gleaming metal, this was a cavalryman's sabre.

"EE-YAH-YAH-YAH-YAH-H-H-H!" he yelled in a changeling's soprano, then leaned low on the gelding and charged.

Up pasture a hundred yards imaginary enemies did their valiant best. They were, strangely, clad in the richest of uniforms. They had shiny new rifles, and each had not one but two pistols, oh pistols indeed! At each belt hung a dagger, loose in its scabbard for instant use if bayonet failed. Even more important, behind them were hundreds of poor penniless peons whom they had enslaved, not a few of these being young girls of rare and tender beauty.

Doroteo the conqueror routed these soldiers in one terrific military action, swept through their lines, released the captives, then swerved on back to reality behind the herd of horses that were in his charge. He reined up, using the single line from his gelding's halter. It was to his credit that he had trained the horse so well. The animal dropped to a liver-jolting trot, then a walk and finally stopped, sides heaving. Doroteo surveyed the battlefield longingly a moment then swung down. He removed the halter and cached it again in a tree, marking well which one. Again he felt that it was a priceless thing. It and the broken pocket knife were almost his only possessions. For the poor garment that he wore—a half-robe, half-shirt sort of thing with short breeches made by sewing it between—he had utter contempt. But it was a covering, and it was all that he had. It was lathered now with horse sweat and he didn't care. The exhilaration of the ride lingered so that no distress rested in him. Until, after a few moments, that eternal worry, that abiding, never-quite-satisfied torment of his life assailed him anew. Hunger.

He studied the sun. That sluggardly ball of the heavens had been loafing, for the hour could be no more than ten. He spat on the grass, stood with hands on his hips, gazing afar. He looked at the horses in his charge and saw nothing wrong; they grazed contentedly, not deeply as sheep or even as cattle graze, but with much moving about, cropping only the top tender new growth, a bite here, a bite there, and with much wasted motion. He admired horses. They were not like fearful cud chewers, such as cows. These would gobble every stick of green grass in sight in the early morning, then hide in shade to belch up and chew their food. This, he knew, was because of mountain lions, of which Mexico had many, and leopards, of which there were a few. Grab food in a hurry, then hide.

"Horses are not afraid," he told the inner Doroteo.

"Yes they are," he was answered, wisely. "But not as much. They can be killed by lions, but they can fight mightily with their heels. And you can ride them. Now, if you *owned* the black gelding, Doroteo—"

There it was again. If he owned something. Owned a horse. It

4

would truly be wonderful. On such a horse, well trained, he could go anywhere, do anything. That is, he could if he had, say, a pistol. Or even a bigger knife. Almost every grown man who rode a horse also wore a pistol, sometimes two. Often these riders wore belt knives as well. Imagine, having a horse, two pistols, and a knife!

But that was too much. That was foolish. Come down to earth, Doroteo. Even if you were grown you could have no such luxury. You are the peon son of a peon widow with many children, you are destined to be a peon worker all your life.

"Why?" demanded the inner boy.

No answer came. Why, indeed? He didn't know the answer.

He spat on the grass again, restudied the sun, and measured his shadow. A little time had passed, yet it still was not midday. But then, a man's lunch weighed heavily in his mind. Perhaps it had gotten dirty! Or soiled by the horse lather when he rode! He felt duty bound to inspect it.

He removed an unwrapped roll from the one pocket in his garment. It was made of three cold, somewhat leathery tortillas. Inside them was a twist of black-red substance, dried to a hard leather state. This was sun-cooked meat. A month ago a horse had fallen off a bridge and had to be shot. Doroteo's mother had been given a hind quarter and with her children had cut the red flesh into finger-sized strings, hung them on wire, guarded them. In a few days they were done. Doroteo relished this meat and bread. He had eaten the same fare for breakfast, and for supper would have it again with maybe a little goat's milk. It was not enough but it was good. He had meant only to inspect the roll of food, but once in his hands it took command. Long before the sun reached its zenith he had gobbled all the tortillas then chewed and sucked and swallowed the dried horse meat down.

It is logical that after a midday meal a man should rest. About noon Doroteo observed that even the horses rested. They had grazed, they were disposed now to hump their backs a little and doze. A few lay down; most slept standing, one's head beside another's tail. This showed intelligence, he knew, for each could swish insects from the other. Cows had no such brains. Cows were peons; driven by hunger, worked at plows and carts, fearful, stupid, beaten down. Horses, now, would buck. They would snort and paw and kick and run away, and rest when it was time

5

to rest, like human beings who owned land. Doroteo admired horses and admired human beings who owned land. He felt a bit uplifted from such meditation, so he joined the noble clan of human beings by lying down in the shade of a palo verde tree. It was only thin shade—the palo verde has negligible leaves—but it was enough. In a matter of seconds he too dozed. But, outdoorsman that he was, if the herd had shown any commotion, made any unnatural noise, he would instantly have been alert.

When he did awake he quickly checked the horses and saw that all was well. The sun had moved over a way now, enough that the tortillas and jerked meat seemed to have evaporated within him, but not nearly enough to hold a promise of supper. Still, he was not without resources; boys of thirteen rarely are, no matter how poor, he had observed.

"There are cactus apples," the inner Doroteo reminded him. He went to a prickly pear cluster nearby. With a green twig bent double he removed a purplish fruit, held it and scraped tiny thorns off with his knife. The bloody pulp and juice inside were tasty; not like candy, but sweetish, and somehow satisfying. A thing sailed through the air beside him then, and with a boy's quick reflexes he pounced onto it, knocked it to earth, grabbed it in his hands. This, too, he ate, raw. He was not proud of eating raw grasshoppers, but this was a huge one, and it helped. An Indian boy had taught him that grasshoppers could be good. They were better roasted, he knew, but he was forbidden ever to make a fire. He caught two more, then ate another cactus fruit. The hunger subsided, so that he glanced back at the horses for reassurance, then lay down again on the grass, content. After all, life had its good moments for Doroteo Arango, he admitted to himself. This was one of them. One of the very few.

The sky today was the same color that shone in the eyes of Señorita Rosie Orellana, Don Felipe's niece. He had—rare bounty —been close to Señorita Rosie one time. The housekeeper at the hacienda had ordered him to bring in wood for the main fireplace, and by chance he had encountered Señorita Rosie there. He had not spoken—he would have been whipped, of course. But he couldn't avoid seeing. She had not smiled. Nothing had happened. Except that she had stared at him with eyes that were not the brown-black of most peons, but they were the rich startling blue of the Mexican sky.

6

That had been almost a year ago, and forever since then he had carried Rosie Orellana in his dreams. Right now, supine on the grass, he saw her in a sky coach. It was cottony and beautiful and drawn by a line of white stallions that curved around a mountain peak to go out of sight. And the master coachman of this remarkable conveyance was—who? None other than Doroteo Arango. Of a surety, none other. For none other could be trusted to hold the diaphanous cloud reins, to guide the stallions and guard the feminine perfection inside the coach. He began humming a little now; singing a little, monotone; a sort of happy chanting, on a hillside, alone, under cloud castles in a cerulean sky.

It was about an hour's walk back to the hacienda, the vast, rambling, beautiful ranch home with its servants' quarters, stables, workshops, and corrals; about an hour if you allowed the horses to amble along, nipping grass now and then, pausing in Arroyo Blanco for a drink, moving quietly. It is never good to hurry a remuda, he knew; the animals may scatter, may even stampede over miles of country, requiring days to round up. If Doroteo allowed his to scatter he would naturally be beaten. However, if he arrived at home before late twilight he might also be beaten for taking some of the animals' grazing time. Thus a wrangler had to gauge time with care. His stomach helped with that. He was already very hungry again before he finally stirred himself. It was at a moment when the sun had a notch cut out of its underside by the saw-tooth mountains that formed a fence for the pasture.

He arose from the grass, stretched himself luxuriously, and would have walked toward the herd when something caught his attention. It was an erratic, bobbing sort of motion on the ground, a human form approaching not a quarter-mile away.

"Leonti!" he muttered.

He said it in frank distaste, and no little alarm. Leonti Soto, the cripple, away out here. It could mean only one thing. But then, it was now time to take the horses homeward, so why had a messenger been sent to summon? The alarm mounted to fear. Leonti, that despicable, filthy, ill-begotten, had not been sent as a messenger. He had been spying. Doroteo thought back. No, there was no need to fear. Not since morning had he broken any rule, not since he had ridden the black gelding. That was long hours ago. Leonti, then, had come on his own for one invariable pur-

7

pose—to molest him. It was an old story. Leonti Soto age eighteen, hip broken and back bent these four years since a grown man had all but killed him, was out to molest Doroteo, as had been tried before. Doroteo watched him approach with utter loathing. What Leonti did to people, what he did to *boys*, was too well known. If he couldn't have his way by persuasion, then he tried it by force.

As for Doroteo, he had learned to handle this outrageous situation. At age thirteen he was no longer afraid of any personal attack from Leonti for he could outrun the cripple, and even felt sure he could out fight him if he should accidentally be caught. If one butted a bigger boy suddenly in the belly, or if one abruptly kicked; with a knee in the groin then broke away—you see? Doroteo had learned some tricks through sheer necessity. Once free from Leonti's clutches, he could stand even a few yards distance and scorn him.

On the other hand, Leonti Soto held the vast power of Don Felipe behind him.

Leonti was the landowner's known informer, probably his favored one. This was common talk. Leonti, no better than the other peons, indeed worse in view of his moral degradation and cunning, was at all times and under all circumstances a creature to be feared. You didn't insult him without assurance of retribution. One word about you to Don Felipe, true or not, could bring the wrath of hades upon you. He wouldn't even have to speak to the don; a tattling to the overseer would be enough to insure the whipping post. Doroteo had seen it happen to others, his own mother included. It was commonly whispered among the 300 or so peons on the rancho that sooner or later somebody would kill Leonti Soto. A knife from the darkness, maybe. A shot from ambush. Better, a sudden, vengeful strangling. Nobody hinted when, or by whom, but all knew why.

Doroteo waited. The crippled boy hobbled on. When he came near the smaller lad he began to grin. Grin, not smile. Doroteo stared straight into his eyes, still waiting.

"I will not let you come any closer," Doroteo said, from ten or twelve yards away.

"I won't hurt you," Leonti answered.

"Because I won't let you. Why are you here? It is just time to

8

start homeward. I will be there in an hour. I will drive the herd and you can't keep up, you know that."

Leonti's grin became broader. "Perhaps if I rode, I could."

"You are not to ride, you know that. Nobody is to ride."

Leonti chuckled, his stooped head bobbing with it. Doroteo, never very clean himself because there was no way to keep clean, nevertheless was repulsed by the older boy before him. Leonti's Indian-black hair was matted with dirt and hung in irregular strings almost to his shoulders. He had on better clothes than Doroteo but these were filty and the smell of him was strong. Doroteo, taking in these details anew just after gazing at the perfection of pasture and mountain and sky, was conscious of the ugliness, the near bestiality. Leonti took another step or two but the lad moved away.

"I said you are not to come near me, no matter what," Doroteo emphasized. "You know why. You are not out here to help me, or to visit."

"We could be friends," said Leonti, emphasizing the could.

"We could not. No."

"Then I must tell you—we had *better* be friends, eh?"

Leonti tilted his head and grinned again, knowingly. The fear leaped anew in Doroteo. He stared, speculating, wondering. He hadn't long to wait.

"The black horse—it rides well, eh?"

Doroteo did not answer.

"Don Felipe will be interested to know the black one has been broken to ride. True, he has expert horesmen for that, for the training."

"I do not know what you are talking about," lied Doroteo, heart pounding now.

Leonti shrugged. "I have just mentioned the black horse, the gelding. You ride him well. Tell me about it, eh? We could be friends, as I said."

Doroteo had to back away from him again. But now he knew. He *had* been seen. Plainly, the hated one had been out this morning, watching. Hidden, probably, in the rocks on the hillside yonder half a mile away. He might have come earlier. Why hadn't he? Doroteo couldn't guess.

"I would pay you not to mention it," said Doroteo.

"Pay me? With what? You never have money, you know that."

9

It was true, of course. Doroteo was bluffing, hoping. "I will get some."

"No. Not you. You couldn't. But now, let me see, have you anything else, maybe? You won't be friends. What have you, then, to offer me?"

What indeed had he? The boy thought fast. His earthly possessions were almost none. Once he had owned a harmonica that must have cost all of twenty-five centavos, but it was much too valuable and had promptly been stolen. He even suspected Leonti of stealing that, though he never heard it played in the peon village. But now, except for the poor broken pocket knife, he had nothing. Or—no! The hidden halter! Now *that* was something. That was a treasure. It was well made, he knew. It had taken him many hours to cut the thongs and plait them and knot them just right. It would be worth maybe a whole *peso*, a dollar. To lose it would break his heart, but then fear of a broken body can be stronger. If it could mean immunity from the whipping post—

"A halter, maybe?" he ventured.

"What kind of halter?"

"The one you must have seen me ride with. It is—well it is strong. I made it. There is even a rosette. It is all I have."

"Let me see it."

"No. Not until I know for sure. You have not seen me ride? You know nothing? You will not tell anyone? You promise?"

"I will say nothing until I see the halter. I can sell a good halter. But a mere piece of rotten string fashioned into a halter—"

That touched Doroteo's pride. "It is no piece of string! It is worth much. I will get it."

He ran fast to the tree in whose foliage he had concealed it, then returned. Leonti nodded approval. He took it from Doroteo, who held it safely at arm's reach; tested its strength and admired its beauty. He fingered the rosette.

"All right," said Leonti, at length, grinning again. "It is a trade."

"You will say nothing?"

The hated one shrugged. "You do not trust me? I have honor. If I say it is a trade, it is a trade. But the sun no longer shines," he concluded, significantly.

Relieved of fear once more, Doroteo hastened to start the horses. He ran to them, then gently began the driving. They were

10

in passive mood. A gentle old mare led them, as always. She pointed her Roman nose homeward and the others filed in behind, the sway-back gelding near the rear. Doroteo eyed him longingly. Common sense told him that he, the wrangler, should ride. There was no reason, except the ranch overseer's orders, why he shouldn't ride behind the remuda to and from the pasture each day. But that would amount to privilege. That would set him above the other peon workers, who perforce must have no luxuries, no consideration at all.

"We are worse than cattle," murmured Doroteo. From the inner Doroteo came the reply—"One day you will go away from this, one day you will rescue your mother and your sisters and flee."

It was an old dream, a thing to focus the mind on when trying to sleep at night. He glanced back now. Leonti was hobbling homeward too, carrying the prized halter. Leonti represented the power that ground the other peons down; power and treachery. In the dust from the hoofs Doroteo spat his contempt for Leonti. He would make another halter, if ever he could find any cowhide again.

The sun was wholly gone when he put the horses in their corral for the night and went to his mother's adobe hut. No light shone from it, for this would have been a waste of oil, but the mother and the brothers and sisters were waiting.

"You are all right, Doroteo?" his mother asked. "You are not hurt? Sick?"

"No, Madrecita. I am fine."

It was her regular query, to know if her children had made it safely through one more day.

"Then let us eat," said she, and arose from the doorstep where she had been sitting.

By the dim night glow she served them, making no comment. Each heard rather than saw the others eating. They had tin plates with fresh, tasty tortillas on them, but tonight she had added a stew, hot and savory. They knew she had made it by boiling some of the jerked meat, chopping it, adding chili pepper and a potato or two. It was delicious. It was a treat. It filled the belly and gave one a sense of well-being. Doroteo almost forgot about losing the halter. Fortunate was he, he told himself, that he had *had* a halter with which to bribe the older boy. Suppose he had had

11

nothing, save maybe a rotten rope halter indeed! Then he could never have bought immunity from punishment. On his bed of corn shucks and canvas on the packed dirt floor of the house, he slept well, beside two brothers.

At dawn, too, peace rested within him. There was talk in the family. Small talk. The little mother—*madrecita* she was called by all the children—hummed as she prepared breakfast. It was a pleasure to watch her flap the tortillas from hand to hand, shaping them and giving them the texture to cook well and taste well. She baked them outdoors on a piece of sheetmetal over a few coals of fire, and fresh from this stove they were more than good, they were delicious. Doroteo knew that his sisters ground the corn for them in a *metate* with a *mano*, Indian fashion, and that the grinding was not considered drudgery, but was more like fun. You knelt before the big hollowed-out rock, grasped the stone firmly, and moved it over the corn in rhythmical washboard motions, and you sang as you worked, emphasizing the body rhythm—

> *NOW we GRIND our CORN for DIN-ner*
> *NOW we COOK and EAT and SAY*
> *THANKS to GOD for FOOD and MER-cy*
> *GIV-en TO us DAY by DAY.*

There hadn't been any too much mercy, Doroteo felt. He never said so; madrecita or the village priest would have scolded him severely. What is mercy, anyway, he often wondered? Well, it was something not to be sick with tuberculosis, or maimed from an overseer's cruelty like Leonti Soto, or in jail like several men he knew. But it was not mercy to be hungry all the time, or to be beaten, or to shiver with cold all winter even in your bed.

He did not think in such vein this morning, though. He was content. He had escaped punishment by a bit of bribery and he had slept well, and he had a full belly to start the day. He stuffed his tortilla-and-jerked-meat lunch into his pocket again and departed for the remuda. Don Felipe wanted the horses on pasture before the sun actually showed its fiery face above the hills. Horses grazed early.

The cowboys and the wagon drivers had already cut out what stock they needed for the day, but half a dozen men waited at the corral gates as Doroteo approached this morning.

12

"Hola," said one. "There he is."

All turned to look at Doroteo. They were rough men, some barely grown, one or two older, with mustachios. All were in dirty work clothing, and all wore shoes because they were riders and you could not work cattle well if you were barefooted. Of one accord they began to grin, but it was not a friendly greeting. One of them stepped out to meet the thirteen-year-old wrangler.

"Well, my little friend," said he. "It is you, eh? You are ready to ride to work, eh? You are grown, maybe? A cowboy, a caballero. You will *ride* behind the remuda this day, eh?"

Doroteo stopped, panic stricken.

So they knew! The speaker here was a foreman, a range boss of low sort but invested with almost unlimited powers. Doroteo had already learned to hate him. Now he beheld the man with wide-eyed fear. It was well justified.

In one sudden motion the man reached out and slapped Doroteo to the ground. The others laughed.

No more words were spoken. Doroteo did not cry out, did not say anything. Slowly he got to his feet, backing away. Instantly the man darted to him and slapped him down much harder than before. In the same moment he straddled the boy and reached both huge hands to strike him—*slap-slap-slap-slap*—on the head and face, back and forth as the mother had slapped her tortillas. Then he stepped back, waiting.

Doroteo, dazed by the punishment, could not rise for a minute or so. The men found much humor in his writhings there on the dirt. Finally he regained his feet. He still had made no outcry; he shed no tears. He began brushing dirt off his garment, his hair, his face and arms. His lunch, the unwrapped tortillas and meat, had fallen unnoticed to one side. A dozen or more workers about the barns, the corrals, the huts, the fences, had paused to watch the punishment, but none dared interfere, none spoke or gave protest.

"I think not," said the foreman, answering his own sarcastic questions. "I think you will walk, as before. I think the black horse will walk and graze this day without you on its back. And if you do not like it, I can see how you like the feel of my hands some more."

Nothing else was said. Doroteo took it as dismissal, and so opened the corral gate, went in and quietly started the animals again toward their valley pasture. As he came back out behind them he saw Leonti Soto sitting atop the corral fence. Leonti was grinning, chuckling silently, his twisted body shaking a little with his triumph. He held Doroteo's beloved halter across his knees, as if to taunt him.

"Good morning, Doroteo," said Leonti. "Doroteo, my friend." And his body shook with increased laughter at that.

Doroteo ignored him, staring straight at the horses filing away. He did not look back. Soon he could not be seen, in the dust cloud behind the walking herd. The people around the area dispersed to their own assigned duties for the day.

For the first time in his life Doroteo Arango wanted to kill somebody. Two somebodies. In the bitterness of his feelings he kicked the dirt, adding to the dust cloud raised by the horses, his mind seething with plans. Dust entered his mouth, his nostrils, his eyes and ears. He ignored it, because he was envisioning just how he would like to slay Leonti Soto and the foreman. He had no weapon except his broken knife, but perhaps it would be enough. He would have to think it out.

He decided the knife of itself had too short a blade, but it was kept sharp and so another idea developed. With the blade he could slowly whittle and scrape a stout limb of dried mesquite until it was shaped like a dagger. This would give him something to do, something to occupy his mind. When it was finished, he could then watch for the opportune moment to strike. This would not be hard in the case of Leonti Soto, who was stupid anyway, he felt. Leonti could be lured into the distant fields by a hint of "love," as Leonti called it.

There he, Doroteo, could ambush him; stab quickly—then many times, once for each remembered insult and act of perfidy—and finally throw the body into a crevasse. Or no, let it lie. Let it lie in the open so that buzzards could enjoy it. He, Doroteo, could in turn enjoy watching the buzzards pluck out dead Leonti's eyeballs, and watching them tear into his belly, their feathered bodies leaning back with each pull by the fierce beaks.

Killing the grown foreman would require more study. Yet even now he had a sort of plan forming. He would wait a week, maybe two. Then he would quietly say to the foreman that a woman, a pretty woman, was out in the grazing area with a message for him. "You are to come there at noon tomorrow," he would say.

He knew that would lure the foreman out, alone. He wasn't just sure why it would, but it would; he had seen many ways in which men reacted to messages and hints and flirtations from women. Men always obeyed such a summons. Maybe it was like his own strange new feelings about girls; like he himself had reacted when he saw Rosie Orellana, or even when he saw her in the clouds, in his dreams. Her vision alone could generate a powerful stirring inside him, and it was pleasant, indeed it was more than pleasant, it was exciting. He had no words for these things, but instinct told him the same feelings carried on into manhood, perhaps stronger and stronger. Yes, he could lure the foreman out.

He wasn't sure, yet, how he would kill the foreman. He saw the wooden dagger in his mind, yet he couldn't simply walk up boldly and stab a grown man. Maybe, first, with a heavy rock—he could throw a rock as big as his two fists with deadly accuracy, for a few yards. He had learned that by much practice, for fun, then had used it repeatedly to kill a rattlesnake or a rabbit. He knew that he could hit a man on the head, and that it would stun the man. And the. . . .

Nothing came of it. By noon he felt exhausted. By nightfall he had abandoned his lurid plans, because just the thinking of them, acting the killings out in his mind, had seemed to ease his anguish. Besides which, the daughter of another peon worker had slyly followed him to the grazing grounds that day.

She appeared by magic, as if she had been a mountain wraith, late in the afternoon. She must have moved like the Indian she was, he realized, for he had seen nothing, heard nothing, until he was alone and sitting in the cool shade of a boulder watching his horses graze, then suddenly she was there. His mouth popped open as he sat erect, but he could only stare at her.

She was not pretty. She was not even remotely like Rosie Orellana. But she was a girl, who looked older than her age, and his eyes widened as she dropped her single garment to the ground.

"I have come," said she, simply, "to show you something, give you something."

It was his first direct experience, and he found it so diverting that the thought of slaying the two men receded in his mind. For days thereafter, when alone, he thought not of them but of her.

15

2

ON THIS brightly beautiful morning in October of 1890, young Doroteo Arango walked out of his mother's adobe home and flexed his arm muscles proudly. He looked at his two sisters, Martina and Mariana, and saw that they were pretty. He looked at his two brothers, Antonio and Hipolito, and saw that they were strong though not so strong as he. He felt especially good this morning, and for reason. His mother came toward him, smiling.

"Congratulations, Teo," said she. "You are fifteen years old today."

There in the yard they made a little ceremony of it. It held an unwonted seriousness, actually, but then he sensed that they were shy. He, Doroteo, had not always been gentle and kind. As elder brother it was necessary at times for him to whip the younger ones, or to shout maledictions at them. Nevertheless he felt himself respected, even loved, and today he loved them all in turn. Martina, the youngest, came to him holding a little package.

"Happy birthday," she said. "From all of us."

That embarrassed him, so he tried to be nonchalant. "Thanks," said he, shrugging, but accepting the package. It was wrapped in a poor piece of red paper with no ribbon tie, but that didn't matter. He knew it was all they could find; to have bought something was out of the question. In truth, he was astonished to receive any gift at all. He opened the paper and took out a belt.

It was pretty. It was made of seven thin strings of leather artfully woven together and had a steel buckle that must have cost them several cents. So they had sacrificed. They had given up something, had worked in secret to make the belt, and had bought the buckle for it. Now that was good. He felt touched.

"*Gracias,*" he said, with more feeling this time. "Thank you, Madrecita."

He had to turn away, then, because he was afraid he might cry. His emotions could get out of hand easily. A man of fifteen does not cry, he told himself; he is not a baby. But—some things

16

could upset his resolutions; some things inside him.

These things inside him were Doroteo's great burden of late. At age fifteen or so, no boy is his own master, a priest had told him; if he is normal, he is at once controlled, harassed, and inspired by strange little chemical factories in his body. Teo had long felt his factories working. And while they distressed him, he sensed that they also made him very strong.

"You are already a better man than your father was," a co-worker on the ranch had told him recently. "Augustin Arango was a good man. But he was weak, and you are like an ox, Teo. You can become a better farmer than he."

Doroteo was not pleased with that. He had no intention of becoming a farmer. He was already a rancher, from necessity, from years of enforced labor. The time was nearing when he would be free. How? He wasn't sure. He only knew he would free himself. He had first sworn it back when he was age thirteen and a foreman had whipped him.

Such was, in truth, his dedicated purpose now. He thought of it practically all the time. Even when he was seeking pleasure the thought of escaping, of rebelling against the rich landowner, was uppermost in his mind. He couldn't just run away and leave his mother and the other children. Not yet; not until they were further along, or until he was driven to it, maybe. But the time would come. The love they held for him, and he for them, was symbolized in the birthday belt, so that the ties were strong. But he weighed almost one hundred and sixty pounds already and that was more than many grown men weighed. He could tighten his arm muscles and see their beautiful bulge. He could lift things that some of the too-fat grown cowboys couldn't lift. And it had been over a year now since he had last been approached by the despised Leonti Soto. The approach, made where Doroteo had been resting from a gruelling day of work, had caused Doroteo no alarm. He had simply reached both hands for the older boy's neck, grasped it firmly and started shaking.

"And if you so much as whisper a word, if you try to tell any overseer or anybody else," Doroteo had threatened, and meant it, "I will catch you again this way. When I turn loose, you will be as dead as a gutted steer." Leonti had believed him.

Before age sixteen Doroteo had enjoyed many girls. That first homely one, when he was but thirteen, had asked nothing in re-

17

turn, and they had met often; then her family and she had moved far away and out of his life. He felt that she had taught him much. When he was fourteen another had replaced her in his life, and shortly after he was fifteen he had such confidence, such strange new force and outpouring, that he found himself welcomed by a very special beauty among the peons. She too asked nothing in return. They met again and again, and so far as he could see she got the same enjoyment and release that he did. Soon he was emboldened to approach other girls, and found them willing.

This, then, became the second most dominant thing in his life. By the time he was sixteen, the powerful determination to achieve freedom from peonage was almost matched by the recurrent and overwhelming desire for girls. One need, one yearning, somehow aided and encouraged the other. He accepted their inevitability and began to plan his life in accordance with their increasing demands.

One afternoon shortly before his seventeenth birthday, he was shoeing horses in the ranch blacksmith shop. A man entered and looked carefully around. Nobody else was present, the smithy having gone for the day. The man was perhaps forty years of age, and an inch or two taller than Doroteo. The boy, stooped over with a horse's hoof resting on his knees, and holding a hammer ready to nail on a shoe, looked up questioningly.

"I'm going to kill you," said the man, as simply and directly as that.

Doroteo reacted instantly. The man had reached inside his coat to draw a pistol, but in the same instant Doroteo's right arm made a fast arc and let the hammer fly. It struck squarely in the belly. The man, startled as if himself shot, grunted a sudden *"UNH-h-h-h!"* and doubled up. He had hardly struck the floor before the boy had the pistol in his own hand. But he did not shoot it. He just held it ready, and finally threw a bucket of dirty water from the blacksmith's tub onto the man. This revived him so that he got up and hastened away, aware of his narrow escape from the same death he had come to administer.

That was the first father who ever sought revenge on Doroteo Arango. Nothing came of it, for the man was hurt in an accident next day and soon moved on. But Doroteo acquired, in that manner, the one possession which he had most craved during all his boyhood—a gun.

18

Several times he had shot guns. Older workers on the ranch, impressed recently by the lad's strength and skill at handling horses, had taken a liking to him. These had let him shoot their pistols and rifles. Once he had gotten to go hunting and had brought home a better bag of game than the man who accompanied him.

"He shoots as if he was born to it," that man reported, with some pride. "I showed him just once how to line up the sights. He had no practice. He just started shooting when the quail arose."

He wasn't much interested in having a shotgun, he told himself. A rifle and a pistol, yes, but a scatter gun, no. Now at long last he had a pistol. He kept it hidden for two months after the incident in the blacksmith shop. Nobody made any move to claim it. He made discreet inquiry about the owner and learned that the man and his family had been gone for weeks. "The daughter was with child," a man told him. "They wanted to go away."

With child! Doroteo felt a peculiar masculine exhilaration. With child, *his* child! He was sure of it. He had fathered a child, and that proved something, eh? That proved he was a man, didn't it? To be sure, yes. It had been a pleasure. True, a man was expected to—well, to take care of his own child. But this was different. This was not the same as if he were married to the girl and they had set in to raise a family. This was *her* business, her idea. This child, now—he could take pride in having fathered it, yet he would probably never see it, never need to know it existed. Somehow that seemed like a very satisfying arrangement. He began to boast of it to the other gangling, grinning adolescents on the ranch and found that it did indeed add to his prestige. He did not specify which girl, he just told his friends that he knew for sure, because the father had tried to kill him. And that he had taken the father's gun away. When he exhibited the gun, it was proof complete.

Teo Arango, then, knew that he acquired stature on the big ranch. If he swaggered a little more than heretofore, it was only natural, he felt, and was not unbecoming. Before he realized it he had become a sort of minor overseer or boss in his own right. "You, Arango, will see to it that the work is finished before sundown," the ranch foreman had casually mentioned, in dispatching eight of the younger men to a distant job one day. Teo, thus ap-

19

pointed, stepped into leadership. The job was finished by mid-afternoon and the crew back home by 4 p.m. When the foreman would have assigned further work for the day, Teo spoke up.

"We've done our day," he announced, with firmness. "You said sundown, and we've beat that time. Now we are tired, understand? We do no more today."

It was heresy. It was rebellion. It was direct challenge. But he observed that the foreman quite without realizing it fell into line. Where he might have ordered and gotten the whipping post for Doroteo Arango, he just glanced at the big seventeen-year-old standing there feet apart, hands on hips, waiting, then said, "All right." He walked away as if something else entirely was on his mind.

The crew of peons was utterly dumbfounded. When it became apparent that no punishment was to follow, they turned to Teo with increased respect. He ignored them, strode toward his mother's home, happy in his new stature.

"That Teo," one muttered. "He is *mucho hombre, no es verdad?*"

Mucho hombre. Much man. Much man, indeed.

Teo made himself pay little attention to the momentary triumph. His good sense told him it was more accidental than otherwise; that the foreman had been preoccupied. It probably would not happen again. Or—maybe it would, he decided; he, Teo, was a man grown tall here lately. He had considerable hair on his face and was doing well enough with a mustache for Margarita Monrovia to have noticed it.

"I should like to be kissed by your new whiskers," she had told him at the *baille* last Saturday evening.

He had kissed her so hard and long that her upper lip was a little bloodied, and she had pushed away from him with fire in her eyes. But it hadn't hurt his popularity any, he discovered. He had kissed half a dozen other girls before the last song was sung, and when he moved through the door of the barn-ballroom, the other boys, large and small, had stepped respectfully back to make room for him. This was good. This was tonic for his soul.

He acquired cartridges for his pistol by the simple act of entering a storage room one day and walking off with a carton of them. The carton was too heavy to conceal under a coat, and he was in no mood for concealment anyway. He felt defiant. He

20

did know that no overseer or other person in authority was around at the moment, but he also knew that a dozen or so fellow peons saw him. For these he felt disdain. He picked up the ammunition—the word "steal" did not enter his mind—and walked boldly out, scowling. He had no qualms of conscience. Something inside him told him constantly now that, over the years, he had given Don Felipe the ranch owner far more in terms of labor than had ever been paid him or his mother in wages. Thus he considered himself entitled to take a few things. And he was sure no peon would report what Teo Arango had done.

He was a full-time cowboy these days, mounted, with shoes. This gave him prestige in the ranch social life. He was able to spur his horse, lean forward and rope a bull calf, dismount and tie the calf in a matter of twelve to fifteen seconds. This gave him almost championship stature among the other cowboys. He had a good knife, too. It was furnished him by the ranch foreman as a necessary tool. One blade was long and pointed, excellent for digging screwworms out of cattle, boring holes in leather and such. Another blade was shorter and rounded at the end, and razor sharp. This was for castrating. He taught himself to castrate a bull calf with no help at all, also in a matter of seconds. He also could build a quick fire, heat the short-handled stamp iron from his saddle, and put the ranch brand on the calf.

Whenever a branding fire burned and took its few minutes to heat the iron to a pink-red, Teo made opportunity to shoot. Such lone roping, castrating, branding episodes normally took place far from any ranch house, where he could shoot for ten minutes without being heard or questioned. The pistol was heavy, but not too heavy. Its cylinder held six shots. In a matter of weeks he could hit prickly pear ears at thirty paces, firing at one-second intervals. Soon after that he could do almost as well without taking aim, just firing from the hip. He'd stop for a few minutes at sundown, riding in from the range, and blast away at small rocks set on a bigger one. If a chipmunk paused momentarily on a log, sitting up sniffing the air out of curiosity, it likely would be blown to bits by Teo Arango's quick gun. He liked the new feeling of power all this gave him.

The second carton of cartridges taken from the ranch store house was devoted largely to firing from horseback. This developed into a most exciting sport. Teo, mounted now on a very fast bay gelding, would flush a jackrabbit and give chase. The jack could jump up and down, sideways and zig-zag, while still fleeing, and the man who could hit it from a running horse with a pistol was a marksman indeed, Teo knew. Nevertheless Señora Augustin Arango, Teo's mother, had better meat for her table that summer of Teo's seventeenth year. Other game came in, too, enough even to share with friends; Teo's pistol became almost legendary among the ranch workers. It added still further to his growing confidence and prestige.

It also got him in trouble. Whether some despicable traitor told on him, or whether his discovery was an accident, he never knew. One Sabbath morning, on direct orders of Don Felipe who stood by to see them carried out, two powerful men suddenly seized young Teo and bound him with ropes. He had no chance to resist, for a lariat loop descending on him, tightening his arms to his sides, was his first warning. In a matter of seconds he was tied to the whipping post.

"Fifty lashes," ruled Don Felipe, with no word of explanation.

The whip was one of the type used on mules. It was of leather, long, black, flexible, with a ten-inch cracker at the end, a thing of tightly plaited maguey fibres no bigger than a finger and coming to a point. It would make a shot like a pistol if snapped in the air, and would cut like a knife if snapped onto human flesh. Doroteo Arango's faded old shirt was cut to ribbons and blood came from a dozen or more wounds before he was released. He had not cried out. He had not even bowed his head, but just pressed it close to the whipping post. He stepped back from the post stiffly, looked straight at Don Felipe.

For a long, arresting, hate-charged moment the two stared into each other's eyes, Teo stinging with pain and indignation and a ferocious craving for revenge.

"It is not too much price to pay for stolen cartridges," Don Felipe ruled, loftily, averting his gaze. "For sportive shooting when you should have been at work. I do not tolerate thieves and loafers here."

He went into his luxurious home, and Teo to his mother's earthen hut where she could bathe his wounds. The awed onlookers returned without excitement to their own tasks. Another peon worker scourged, they whispered, with a shrug and a tone of resignation. It had happened often before, it was routine. But—to that audacious young Teo Arango? "It bodes ill," murmured one ancient, resting behind his rude shack in the Sabbath sun.

Literally enslaved, Teo worked like a slave on the ranch for a while longer. For one thing he suffered a loss of shoes. This was more than physical punishment, it was symbolic; it advertised the fact that he had been pushed down scale in the petty ranking of workers. His first shoes, the very first he had ever worn (discounting sackcloth and canvas tied crudely around his feet as a boy) had been inherited from his father. As a skilled *vaquero* he had been given shoes because they were equipment for efficient work, just as he had been allowed a fine horse, a good saddle, a top-quality lariat rope, a knife of finest steel. The other things he kept, but the shoes were taken away—amid considerable jeering from the overseers and some from his own more daring peon friends.

He decided to accept the degradation without comment, but he did not smile. He would bide his time. The pistol had been taken away too, of course, so he had no more opportunity to shoot for a few weeks. But one day a friend, a grown man who had respected him, spoke quietly.

"I have a rifle, Teo," he suggested. "I could lend it to you. There are cartridges in the store room."

He mentioned the calibre and type. Teo Arango smiled. Two days later he approached the man and said, "I'd like to borrow that rifle, my friend. Some bullets have been stored in a canyon four miles from here."

In three months he was almost uncannily accurate at rifle shooting. The few friends who dared to slip away with him reported that he could drive a nail stuck into a tree one hundred feet away. A coyote, a jackrabbit, a wolf, a bobcat, glimpsed anywhere in rifle range, usually died in that instant. Señora Arango and the family's friends began to feast on venison.

Teo's prestige thus returned and, along with his muscles, increased noticeably month by month. When he "took" a pair of shoes from the storehouse one day, no mention was made of it by any overseer. When he quietly then boldly refused to accept some of the more unreasonable work assignments, or dared to demand that they be shared with more men, he was not questioned. Even he was surprised that this astonishing development was accompanied by no clash of wills; it was simply as if he were acting

23

naturally, in expected way. The overseers, never very quick witted, could be outmaneuvered without their realizing it. Teo was elated. By the time his nineteenth birthday passed he had become almost an overseer in his own right. His inherent bent toward leadership, toward commanding and being obeyed, had grown along with him and become an accepted thing. He felt proud, and acted older than his years.

A part of this change, this growth in body and capabilities, he felt was due to a change of setting. The Señora Arango's family had, in effect, been "sold." Not literally so, for slavery by name was illegal in Mexico; but in point of fact. They had been sent to live and work on the ranch of the powerful Lopez Negrete family at Hacienda de Gogojito in Durango. Don Augustin Lopez Negrete was perhaps the most arrogant of the landed aristocrats. The Arangos had not bettered their condition, but had worsened it, through no choice of their own. In sheer desperation Teo as head of his mother's family began using his brain to outwit the Don's overseers. He did not always succeed.

One noon he was charged with taking a pair of sox to wear in his shoes—an unheard of luxury for one of his standing, hence a colossal presumption. Since he had the sox on, he was already convicted. It made no difference that the sox had enabled an injured foot to heal. He would have to pay more money than he possessed to escape punishment. A powerful, resentful young man now, he acted on impulse. He ran away.

Don Augustin always acted on the theory that "once a slave always a slave." He simply ordered his older foreman to go bring back the rebellious Arango boy and teach him a lesson. They did so, but at much inconvenience and effort on their part; he led them a chase over one hundred miles, and might still be running but for the sore foot. When they finally brought him home, trussed with ropes across a saddle like a slain buck, they were more than willing to punish him. Don Augustin decreed "as many strokes as you will," and the whipping they gave him at the post this time left scars that he carried to his grave.

Many thought him dead that twilight when they cut him loose and his form slumped inert to the ground. When the bestial men who whipped him walked out of sight, Teo's mother ran from her hut and flung herself on his prostrate form, wailing as if he were dead indeed. But he was not dead; the world would yet hear

24

from Doroteo Arango, he swore there in the dirt. Next morning he reported back for duty, erect, defiant of the pain that still racked him, his eyes half closed and his lips taut in an obvious effort at self control. Don Augustin and his henchmen came near, silently taunting him. He might have killed any one in man-to-man combat for he was now strong enough, his arms and shoulders developed far beyond the average, his back and legs powerful. But he said nothing. "To the fields," ordered the Don, and he started obediently away.·

Hatred, however, glowed in Teo like fire in a volcano's bowels. Mother Arango prayed for him and over him, pleading. He gave no sign save tight-lipped trembling vows of vengeance. Against whom? Don Augustin Lopez Negrete? Not him alone. Against all the don's kind. Against all of Mexico's landed gentry, the overlords, the enslavers who felt that peonage was an institution for their aggrandizement. Against poverty and filth and ignorance and disease and human misery in any form. Young Teo, a mighty power already, knew that he was nearing the time when he would inevitably burst loose.

His next move, he decided, was to run away again; it was the only thing he could do. This time he fled in secret and went far. Traveling barefoot, sleeping under any friendly bush or tree, eating whatever of food he might steal or find, he made his way to Chihuahua City.

He came into this picturesque state capital at night and, knowing he must find work, knew also that he was unspeakably dirty. He could not ask for a job looking like something from a hog wallow. But across the town, then, as for some two hundred years past, stretched the great water flume built by Spanish pioneers. It was a stone ditch, sometimes on the ground and sometimes on beautiful archways, carrying drinking water to the residents there. Any housewife was free to go dip her bucket full as need arose. In this cool, clear river water, then, Doroteo Arango bathed, washed his clothes, and lay hidden nearby until they had dried next morning. By noon he was asking for a job.

An employer quickly hired Teo to drive a freight wagon between Chihuahua City and Guenacevi, at more pay than the boy had ever envisioned. He was astounded, and a sudden new happiness settled upon him. He made two or three trips without mishap, collected his high wage, and felt secure from the oppressions of

25

Don Augustin. Hope, vague but eternal and priceless, brightened his life. Maybe he could soon send for his mother, brothers and sisters, maybe he could work out a better existence for them all.

He had not reckoned on the far-reaching influence of Don Augustin. The don's men learned where Teo was working, and Teo was arrested on a completely false charge of thievery, beaten severely again, and thrown like an animal's carcass into a miserable village jail. He almost died there of starvation and neglect. Months passed, and the only persons to befriend him were fellow prisoners, most of these being outlaws of the worst possible type.

He became very much interested in one of these jailmates because the fellow had some education and an outside friend who brought books and newspapers in. Moreover, he began to read these to the likeable if embittered Doroteo Arango.

"No matter what you do," this one told Teo, "you will be punished if you are a peon. You can read about it all over Mexico. Here, see for yourself." He held a newspaper out to Teo.

The boy smiled his thanks but shook his head. "Maybe you can read, but I can't," said he. "Nor write either."

"You do not need to write. But it is good if you can read, I say. You learn things nobody will tell you. I read for you, what you say?"

"Thank you kindly, my friend," Teo nodded.

"I tell you what—I read to you here what it says about the great Parra."

"The great who?"

"Parra, the bandit. Ho, you have not heard of *him?* Where have you lived, man?"

"Read to me of him, please."

"He is the famous outlaw who is not really an outlaw. He robs only the rich, and gives to the poor."

"He does?"

"Surely, my friend. He is not afraid of anybody. He is very strong. He is a great rider and has good riders with him. When they attack a ranch, they never get hurt."

"They—they take the ranch owner's property, eh? Food, maybe, eh? And clothing? And give it to poor people?"

The jailmate nodded. "That and more. They take money and give *it* to the poor. This Parra is a saint, if you ask me. Here, I will read to you of his latest good deeds."

Doroteo listened intently. It was a version of gallantry and outlawry, a romatic narrative of a personality who seemed to combine all the strength, courage, and idealism of which Teo himself had dreamed. The boy was deeply impressed. When the newspaper reading was done, he gazed off through the jail bars, doubled one fist and drove it into his other palm, murmuring between clenched teeth—"One of these days. . . . One of these days."

The day was to come sooner than he had hoped. And in a manner wholly unexpected.

He served a six-month sentence in this hellhole of a jail, for a crime he had not committed. And when released he still did not go back to Don Augustin's ranch to labor as a slave. Defiant once more, but much more wary now, he got work on other ranches, never staying long in one place, collecting his few dollars in pay and saving them by sleeping in hay lofts and eating whatever he could find. If he caught any hint of danger he disappeared, only to find work elsewhere. Soon he was working as a laborer in Chihuahua City again, but under another name and with a full-blown mustache that effectively disguised him. He did well at this job and found himself with several dollars ahead. In a matter of months he had enough to purchase a horse and—more important —a pistol. On Sundays he took the pistol up the cliff walls of El Rio Chuviscar and practiced shooting again. The skill had not left him, indeed his marksmanship seemed almost uncannily good. It deeply impressed the fellow-worker friends he allowed to accompany him, he noticed. He learned, too, that given a few kind words, a few vague promises, they seemed to idolize him. He resolved to use this power.

One week-end he rode his horse rather boldly out to the ranch of Don Augustin Lopez Negrete, tethered the horse near the houses, and stole into his mother's home.

"Teo!" the younger children shrieked in hearty welcome, running to hug him. Next moment his mother was hugging him and sobbing and laughing all at once. They had feared him dead.

"I bring you money, Madrecita," said her big son.

The few dollars were a godsend. They were unbelievable. They were manna from heaven. They so overwhelmed her and the younger ones that he himself cried in happy unison with them.

"You are nearly twenty," mother reminded him. "You are a

man, Teo. You are a *good* man. Your father would be proud of you if he could know."

"Soon I will come for you and take all of you away," he promised.

"How will you do that? How, Teo?" The children were eager.

"Never mind. I know a way. I am making money. I will bring some more, and some more, as I can. Then one fine day I will have still more and we shall all leave here, and no one can stop us. This I promise by the Holy Mother, by the Infant Jesus and the great God of us all."

He was very impressive and he meant every word he said. Soon he slipped out and was gone again, leaving happiness in the home of his rearing. He made half a dozen or so such clandestine trips to help his mother's family, without being caught or seen. They were spaced several weeks apart. He enjoyed them immensely, not only because of the help he could give his family and the love that he got in return, but because of a growing sense of freedom and power. His heart was full, but so was his mind. He made plans, great plans, yet was now intelligent enough to bide his time. He would have to move with care.

3

IN A CANTINA on the outskirts of Chihuahua City one evening a pleasant, quiet man approached Teo Arango and said, "Are you Jesus Benavides?"

Instantly Teo was alert, ready to flee. But he made no move. His powerful hand gripped the rail of the bar at which he was standing. He eyed the man intently. "Who are you? Why do you ask?"

The man shrugged. "I'm a postman, I deliver mail. It is nothing to me one way or another, but someone said you were Jesus, and I have been looking for him. I have a letter, but he was not at the address on the letter, and so I thought—"

"A letter? For me?" Teo relaxed.

"If you are Jesus Benavides."

28

"I am. Give it to me, please, señor."

"Ho, it is at the postoffice, my friend. I do not carry federal mails into cantinas at night. But tomorrow, eh? What is your new address?"

Teo told him. Jesus Benavides was one of four names he had used, and the one he had left with his mother. He had not expected a letter. But he got this one next evening when he returned from work. He was excited and walked up the street holding it and looking at the inscription. It was beautifully written, with many ink flourishes. He walked faster, curiosity and anxiety riding him. Presently he was in the main plaza and there found what he sought, a public scribe.

"Señor," he began at once, "I have here a letter, and while I can read well myself, I thought—I thought perhaps if you—"

"Of a surety, my young friend. Sit down. It is well for a licensed person such as I to read a letter, as a witness you understand, even though you read well, as of course you do. I can tell by your face that you are an intelligent citizen."

"Yes sir. I will be honored to have you read as a witness."

"So. I will read it aloud twice to you, and make record of the reading if you say so, then write any answer you wish. You—uh, are now employed, eh? A fine, strong-looking young man."

Such a preliminary was quite in custom, an accepted approach and reception, Teo had learned. Each knew that Teo could not read, yet each knew he must save face in the matter by the polite pretense.

"I have some money, yes sir," Teo nodded, understanding.

"Ten centavos for the reading then—no no, not now, I can see you are a man to be trusted—afterward you can pay me; after you dictate the answer, eh? Now if you will just pass me the envelope—"

The letter was obviously written by another public scribe at the other end. It too had flourishes and was rich with courteous phrases. It began, "My Beloved and Estimable Eldest Son, In Whom I have Much Pleasure and the Greatest Respect, Felicitations:"

So it was from his mother. His heart leaped at the thought. Teo loved Michaela Arango, the "Little Mother" of his home; loved her and loved his sisters and brothers with a continual longing, with a wish and a determination to find them a better life. Whatever could the message from home be? He savored the moment. The scribe, having paused for dramatic effect, peered at him over his glasses, waiting. Then in low, cultured, confidential tones he read to Teo.

His mother simply said that there was trouble at home, a new unhappiness, and could Teo come again to comfort them? It would bring her much joy. That's all. No real news, just a plea for help.

Teo stared off, wondering, his mouth open, distress in his eyes. The scribe coughed genteelly, refolded the paper. "We all have troubles, señor. Probably it is nothing great. No death, eh, or she would have said? No, I beg of you not to despair. You are young. There is an answer? I will write for you because I have pen and paper at hand and your own writing materials will be at your home. This way you can get the letter into the mail quickly. The cost is as nothing. Shall I say you will come at once?"

"No. No señor. I thank you." He put down the few pennies for the reading. "No answer. I will go in person. I thank you."

He was headed back to his mother's home within the hour. Trouble. A new unhappiness. Enough for her to have sent for him. It must then be big trouble indeed, for little troubles would not have required so important a thing as a letter. Yet if someone had been sick or had died, as the scribe had mentioned, she would have said so. He wondered what he might expect.

This time he did not try to conceal himself. Being virtually a grown man now, and with a loaded pistol stuck in his belt inside his shirt, he felt secure. He felt defiant of Don Augustin Lopez Negrete and his hirelings. Was he not a man, with a man's rights? What right had Don Augustin or anybody to say when he, Teo Arango, should come and go? Surely a citizen of Mexico could visit his own mother in peace, especially if she had sent for him. He dared anyone to challenge. On a Saturday in broad daylight he calmly rode up to his mother's cabin and dismounted.

"Teo!"

The brothers and sisters saw him and came a-running; all save one. Martina, now sixteen, held back. There was a sadness on her. Teo hugged them all at once, then individually.

30

"Teo, you are crushing my bones, you great huge ox!" Thus spoke the youngest, laughing.

"An ox does not hug, a bear hugs," he explained, laughing in turn. "I am a bear. You are my little cubs, *no es verdad?* With no father at home *I* am the father."

"You are truly a grown man, Teo," said one, admiringly. "You are bigger than most men. Such arms! Such a chest!"

They laughed together and started toward home. "Where is the Madrecita?" he asked. "She is—she is well?"

"She is not sick. She waits."

The mother was sitting inside on a stool, a plain little work-wearied woman in cheap garment and the expected black cloth over her head. Her eyes lighted with a flash of pleasure as Teo entered, and they stared at one another a long moment. He read a sadness on her face. "You are all right, Madrecita? Every one is all right? Martina does not rush to greet me like the others, does not look into my eyes and smile. She is sick, maybe with the stomach pains, eh? Is that why you write for me?"

The mother held out her arms and Teo knelt to hug her. Affection was genuine in this home; love and tenderness, and the free expression of it. It had always been so even when there had been discipline, Teo recalled. "She is not sick, no," Señora Arango answered, at last. "So many are. So many die with the stomach disorders. The healing woman comes, but still so many die. Yet not one of us, my son, not one of us."

"Then I am a happy man this day. I am home. You wrote of trouble, Madrecita, but if everyone is well—ha! I have some more money for you, and a small gift. I have good work now. Soon, as I promised, I shall be able to—"

She held up a hand to stop his boyish enthusiasm. Anguish was in her eyes and he could not talk it away. He turned to the brothers and sisters, gave each a coin and enjoyed doing so. Then with a smile and a hearty slap on the shoulder for each, he ordered them to go outside. "Begone, you puppies. I would talk with our mother alone. We are grown, we do not romp and roll on the ground. Now go and let us old dogs rub noses."

They tumbled out and Teo sat cross-legged on the dirt floor beside her. Once more he looked intently at her face, then he spoke. "Don Augustin. He has beaten you, or one of the children. Or had you beaten. Do not try to say it. I know! The end of that

31

is near, I tell you! With my own hands will I cut the vitals from him, and soon. I swear it, Madrecita. We are not beasts to be whipped and tortured and—"

"Teo!" She halted his outburst of fury. "It is not that. It is no beating. Nobody is whipped."

The young man exhaled, waiting. "Well then?"

"Martina—your sister Martina—"

"Yes?"

The mother was about to burst into tears. Her son stared straight at her, but for her to say what must be said was a difficult thing. She lowered her eyes, bowed her head, put her hands to her face, and finally whispered the awful truth. "Martina . . . . is with child."

For an endless interval he made no sound. But a fire had leaped within him. The mother felt rather than saw his great inhalation, felt the breath expelled, sensed his mighty effort at self-control. He put a hand on her knee, a moment of communion.

"Martina, little Martina," he murmured, at long last. "Who was it, mother? Who is the man?"

"I do not know."

Again they were silent for a long while, then Teo arose. "You will please prepare us some supper, Madrecita, for I am hungry. You are not to cry. I am here now."

He went outside where the smaller children were waiting, eager for play. He seemed not to see them. He went to the corner of the hut, rested one arm on it, and stared out into space. The children sensed his mood and let him be. He stood there a long, long time. When he finally turned it was because the mother had called them to supper; he still had not spoken to any one.

The meal was cheerless. The children ate in silence but every one stared covertly at Teo's face. It was set, stern, glowering. Best go away, he told the young ones, and let the grown people be. They did go away. Martina, having said nothing whatsoever, cleared off the few humble dishes and herself started to go.

"Wait here please, my sister," Teo ordered, gently. "Madrecita, I would speak with Martina."

When the two were alone, he looked straight at her and made his demand. "You have not told my mother who he is. I will not put up with such a thing and you know that. I do not think it was one of the workers, for most are our friends. And you have

32

not been off the rancho. I can ask other people, Martina, but I want it from you. I think it can only be one man."

He waited, but her head was bowed as her mother's had been, and she made no reply.

"You are sweet to hear when you sing, my sister. You are plump and pretty and have pink on your cheeks from the bloom that is in you. Your breasts hold out your dress and the points of them are plain to see. They would not have escaped the notice of any man, Martina. But only one—only one on this rancho—. Martina, I ask you to tell me the truth. Is it the son of Don Augustin?" When she made no reply, made no move, he grasped her shoulders and shook her a little. "*Is it*, I say?"

Martina nodded.

She felt the hands grip with a sudden surge of power, felt him tremble. She began sobbing and fell against him, and with one arm he held her to his breast with a bearlike fury indeed, and with the other he doubled a fist and shook it in the direction of the hacienda, the ranch owner's home. She dropped down to hug his knees in supplication. "Please, Teo, you will do nothing," she begged. "You will only be killed yourself and you will not help me. You are not to blame."

He kissed the top of her head and broke her hold on him and left her crying there on the floor. It was like a scene from a cheap stage play, he realized, for he had seen such things for twenty-five centavos in Chihuahua City, with the heroine sobbing and the hated man of the story leering and the true lover developing a rage. He had felt himself superior to such melodramatics, and a slight contempt for his fellow workers who took them seriously. Were the play actors not just pretending? Of course, my friends; just play acting. It is fun to watch them, but we of course know better, eh? We would not carry on so.

Now suddenly his sophistication was punctured; was limp and unsustaining, like a carnival balloon. This was life itself. His rage was far from any cheap theatrical thing; it was all-consuming, it was monumental, it was demanding. Nor could he run to his beloved Madrecita for guidance in this crisis; he was a man grown tall, and *she* had begged comfort of *him*. It took him a while there to absorb this fact, to realize his new position. Then abruptly he slapped his thigh in anger, breaking his meditations; this was a thing for a real man to handle, alone.

33

Teo Arango took no action that night. No one would have censured him if he had acted then and there, he knew. Instead he went directly to bed. He lay on the crude corn-shuck mattress on his mother's floor, and if he did not sleep until long after midnight he at least rested his travel-weary body. Probably only the little children slept, for he heard his mother and sister Martina sobbing gently until he himself drifted off. They were asleep when he awoke shortly before Sunday dawn.

Quietly he edged out of the bed, stepping over smaller Arangos, careful to awaken no one. Hunger assailed him but he took no food. He got into his clothes, and carefully stuck his beloved pistol into his belt, under the jacket but still within easy reach. Now he was back on the theatre "stage" again, he reflected grimly. Now he was having to resume his part in the harsh cruelties of life. He was ready. The rage that he had carried to bed had not subsided. The hours that he had lain there thinking had served to crystallize all the years of pent-up hatred for Don Augustin Lopez Negrete and his kind. Well, one of his kind, indeed his own contemptible son, had brought matters to a showdown. Teo had long known it would be coming, one way or another. He and his mother and his brothers and sisters and friends had suffered whippings for trivial offenses over the years, he had been imprisoned without cause, he had been the victim of caste and slavery and exploitation and sheer unadulterated cruelties without end. It was better to be dead than to go on so. It was better to be caught and shot by police.

Perhaps he would not have to be caught. Perhaps he could successfully flee. Perhaps he could move fast, hide in the mountains, and never be arrested at all. Perhaps he could find friends, other peons who had been similarly oppressed, to join him and help defend him if need arose. True, he was only nineteen, but he had the strength and skill of many a grown man, more than most. He felt unafraid of anything that lived and breathed the air. He wasn't sure just *what* he would do after the expected flight this morning, but he felt a strange, reassuring confidence.

As he moved silently to saddle the horse that his brothers had cared for last evening, he relished the fury that burned in his breast. It was now a hot, calculating force, not an impulsive thing. He could think clearly. He knew exactly what he meant to do. Young Negrete, son of Don Augustin, was a known coward. No

34

matter if the man had possessed all the bravery of a Benito Juarez, he, Teo Arango, would have gone straight to him; but he was a lascivious, lecherous man-beast with less courage than a tail-straddling dog, who felt secure in being Don Augustin's wealthy son. He thought himself irresistible to girls. He dressed expensixely, rode arrogantly around the ranch never speaking to any workman unless to give some command. Oh, the young don was well known, Teo reflected bitterly.

With a boldness that was to set the pace for all his actions during the ensuing years, Teo rode straight to his task. Entrance to the hacienda was a little gate with some flowers between it and the house door. Teo's foot, in a heavy shoe, struck the gate hard. This was his first expression of the rage within him this morning. It knocked the fragile thing quite off its hinges and banged it into the front door. Next moment he was kicking on the locked door itself.

The door opened almost at once, an outraged servant having been asleep just inside, on guard. Teo Arango said nothing whatsoever to the excited, babbled query of the servant, he strode on through and into the patio. There he realized he must know where to go, so he turned and grabbed the servant who was futilely trying to restrain him.

"The young don—where does he sleep? *Where*, I say!"

He shook the man so hard that his head bobbled back and forth as if hinged to his shoulders, dazed him so that he could no longer cry out. But he did lift a hand, pointing. Teo let him slump to the floor.

The victim Teo sought had already arisen. And having heard the commotion, young Negrete appeared now at the rear patio gate, dressed for the morning. Perhaps he had been preparing for an early ride. Or perhaps he was even now coming from another assignment. No one ever knew.

"You!" Teo called, sighting him.

The other young man must have recognized Martina Arango's brother, yet he had no time for words. It is doubtful if he was even armed, but that made no difference. The hard, harsh bark of Teo's pistol came twice, deafening there in the patio. Four or five other people, women servants and at least one more man, had run in, awakened by the commotion. They were appalled at the scene enacted in the Sunday's dawning, stood transfixed as

35

young Negrete fell, dead before he struck the ground. Teo Arango put the gun back in his belt, turned without a word, and walked out to his horse again. There he paused just once to look back.

One woman had followed him to the door, one had come to her senses. She saw Teo calmly, almost deliberately mount his horse, saw him scowl in haughty defiance, then spur his animal and dash away.

He rode grimly, yet he was calm and was immensely astonished at himself. Astonished not at what he had done, but at the realization of change within his being. Somehow he felt called.

"There will have to be more," he murmured to his horse. "Many more. Everywhere in Mexico the rich are oppressing the poor."

4

Teo's FIRST IMPULSE was to find safety in distance. If he could only get a hundred miles from the Negrete ranch, he felt, he could not be found. In this year of 1897, to be sure, people moved around more and so word of his being wanted would spread. Nevertheless roads were poor, and any member of the Mexican rural police would find hard going if he tried to track down a strong, desperate young peon. One hundred miles should mean security, he felt.

He had not counted strongly enough on the vicious nature of Don Augustin. One hundred miles? Teo on a good horse made that in less than three days, and within the hour after arrival at a village he heard that "A young man named Doroteo Arango is being sought for killing a wealthy don's son." When asked to state his own name, Teo said it was Diego Nogal, and that he was a teamster who had come looking for mules to buy. Never again was he to use his real name.

For the next month, then, Teo hid out in the hills. He had bought some corn meal and he was able to shoot game for meat. One item he forgot—salt. Fresh meat roasted over an open fire can be exceedingly tasty, but without salt it soon loses much of its charm, he discovered. A craving for salt, plus a growing curiosity to know if Don Augustin's men were still actively pursuing him, caused him to slip into a town one day. He saw groups of other young men and boys loafing around stores, on sidewalks, inside bars. A sudden craving for companionship drove him to join some of them, and here he made quiet inquiry.

"I suppose they have not caught him," one man answered him. "But there is a reward offered."

"A reward?"

"Sure so. Come, I will show you."

A poster was stuck to a porch post in front of a grocery store. Its large heading said WANTED, DEAD OR ALIVE, and underneath it was a description of Teo and his crime. Fortunately the man read it aloud; perhaps he was showing off his ability to read. Teo tried not to show too much interest. He made some joke about hoping he could catch the fellow so as to claim the reward, then walked away.

Almost every day he moved his hideout lest some member of the searching *Rurales* spot his horse or his campfire smoke. Part of the time he was in the Sierra de la Silla not far from the Hacienda de Gogojito where he had once worked and where he had friends. One day he recognized one of those friends out alone, Antonio Lares, a man of honor. So strong was Teo's craving for companionship after weeks of hiding that he startled and almost frightened Antonio by running to him. But he was received literally with open arms.

"You have done a good thing," Antonio reassured him. "No one blames you for killing that man."

"No one, my friend?"

"Well, the rich ones, yes. You understand what I mean. No one of your friends. That Negrete, he was a bitch's pup, he deserved to die. But we fear for you, Teo. You are well? You are eating and are not cold? It is winter time. If you should get sick—"

Teo laughed. He was never sick. He was, he felt, immune to the endless ailments that beset most peons, the stomach cramps, the fevers, the strange maladies that took so many lives of young and old. He was made of steel.

"You have become *mucho hombre*, Teo," said Antonio now.

"So? How is that?"

"You killed an enemy of us who work, never forget that. *We*

37

do not forget it. So you are much man, with us."

"Well now! I had not thought." This was something indeed. Here he was almost a hero, when for weeks he had been berating himself for being a common outlaw. Perhaps being an outlaw was not all bad. Out*law* did not mean out of face and favor, eh? If the law, which is made by the rich, favors the rich, then it is no wrong to break that law when necessary. So Teo reasoned.

"Antonio, it will not do for you to be seen talking to me," he reminded his friend. "Now go and do not mention that you saw me, or you may get in trouble yourself. But please do go to my mother and ask her to flee, before Don Augustin takes out his anger on her. Tell her I said take the children to Rió Grande, near San Juan del Rio. I will see them there, maybe."

During the ensuing month Teo wandered back and forth from the Silla Sierra to the Gamon Mountains, compelled to depend upon luck for his food. Often the luck was not good. And so, driven by hunger, he began to take more and more chances. He never knew exactly what revealed him to the military men now seeking him, but probably it was his daring to slip into a village and beg for a quart or so of black beans. He went incognito, but later decided that some unknowing villager mentioned the strange young man's coming, the officers heard of it and started to backtrack. At any rate Teo suddenly heard a noise near his tiny campfire one day. He looked up in alarm.

"*Alto! Manos arriba!*"

He was looking into three gun muzzles. He had not a ghost of a chance to flee or to draw his own pistol for fighting. They disarmed him, tied him hand and foot like a captured panther, and at seven o'clock that night threw him still bound into a vermin-ridden jail cell. He almost died of cold before morning.

His bonds were cut at daybreak when the jailer gave him bread and water. Teo tried to talk with the man. "What will they do with me?" he asked.

"Hang you. Or shoot you, maybe. You know how things are." The jailer shrugged. "I am a poor man myself, and I understand. But I can not help you, you know that. They will have a trial, in name. But you can be sure of what will be decided."

Of course. Of a certainty Don Augustin would demand and get his death. Well, he had gambled, he had known what to expect, and he still felt that killing the man who seduced his sister Martina was worth the penalty he must now pay.

At about ten o'clock the jailer came again. "You are ordered to work until you go on trial," said he. "You are to come out under guard and grind corn."

That was welcome news; anything was better than just sitting in the miserable cell. In the jailyard was a barrel full of shelled corn and they gave him a large metate and mano for the grinding. This was nothing new; he had seen his mother and hundreds of other women grind corn all his life. He set to work, and he also started thinking. Two armed men guarded him, sitting lazily on boxes nearby. The yard gate was patrolled by a sentinel with a rifle, marching slowly back and forth. Just outside the yard was Remedios Hill, and beyond that nothing much but mountains and canyons and wild valleys, rocks and cactus and trees and thorny shrubs, all the things that make up the rough, rugged face of Mexico.

After an hour the two guards grew weary of watching him and fell to talking, gazing off and growing careless. Teo waited for the moment when they were close together, then like a panther he sprang. *Thupp!* A dull, chilling blow from the hand-stone knocked one guard unconscious in the instant. In the same motion Teo with his left hand grasped the other guard. That one was so startled he made no outcry, and crumpled up under the powerful young prisoner's second blow.

Teo looked at the gate. He had timed the assault for a moment when the sentinel was at the end of his march, out of sight beyond the wall. Miraculously, almost no noise had been made, so Teo raced now on tiptoe. A thing of iron, the gate had not been locked because it was guarded and because carts, men, and riders often had to come and go. It creaked a little as Teo pulled it open and that caused the marching sentinel to turn. As he did so a heavy boot heel smacked into his groin and the rifle was in Teo's own hands. The man doubled up on the earth groaning. In a matter of seconds the escaping prisoner was fleeing up Remedios Hill, thence on down the other slope toward a small river. He had no idea where to go or what route to take.

Beside the river a horse lifted its head to stare curiously at him; a horse unsaddled, unbridled, unfenced. At once Teo's boyhood training served him. Perhaps not one man in a hundred could catch a wild Mexican pony that way, but in barely a minute Teo was astride this one and moving off. He had no way to guide the animal except a tug at the mane and pressure of his knees and heels. He needed no more. Teo Arango, Jesus Benavides, Diego Nogal, the strong young man with half a dozen names and soon to acquire a permanent one, was racing like a centaur for the wild free hills.

Teo soon discovered that his luck had not been complete. The horse was typical of the poor scrubs used in Mexico. He kicked it into the fastest possible run because of his desperate need of flight, but after five or six miles it was exhausted. Even after resting a quarter hour it could barely stand. Teo left it and walked on.

It occurred to him now that he had best make some sort of plan. A horse's trail is easily followed, but Teo reasoned that no one saw him catch the animal, and so the officers would think him still hiding somewhere in the area around Remedios Hill. They would spend the day literally beating the bushes there for him and searching in the houses of the town. They might not find the horse trail until tomorrow if ever, and even then not realize he had been the rider. So he could relax momentarily and make plans.

Sitting there amid the mountain country rocks, the young adventurer suddenly knew an intense longing for his mother's home. It was strong enough that he had to answer it, and so he set out walking toward his mother, brothers and sisters near the place called Rio Grande, not too far away. By night he crept to them, and found what he sought. From them he got love and comfort, from them he garnered a clarity of mind.

A cousin quietly stole for him a good horse, a saddle, considerable food, blankets, a knife, a pistol, and ammunition. Teo still carried the excellent rifle he had snatched from the jail sentinel. These things were enough. Tomorrow, he knew, the authorities would have spread the word of his escape, would come to his mother's house and maintain a watch on it. By dawn, then, he was far away. And despite the murder of Negrete, plus the added offense of breaking jail, a strange new confidence rode with him. He hummed and sang a little as he traveled through the vast wilderness there in the rosy-fingered dawn.

"I will have to live by my wits for at least a year," he told himself. "I must go far away from the clutches of Don Augustin.

After a year he will have wearied of seeking me. The Rurales won't bother much to hunt me after five or six months, for it is too much work to hunt a man if he is prepared to take care of himself."

Teo was prepared. For one thing, he had had a previous experience. He was acquainted with his needs outdoors, with dangers and traps to avoid while hiding in mountains, sleeping in caves, avoiding other human beings. He felt entirely secure, he felt grown.

"In a while I will change my name again and quietly go into some faraway town for more food," he continued his planning. "I have two good guns, I can always get food at pistol point. Yes, of course I can! At pistol point a man can get anything. He has only to be brave and wary. Perhaps I will make a name for myself, eh? Perhaps I will become a *bandido*. I might as well, I am already doomed to death if the law gets me. Now I think of it, I am already a *bandido!*"

He savored that fact. A bandit! He, Teo Arango, penniless son of a widowed peon mother, now a bandit! It was something, eh? He had good equipment, he had strength and nerve. He could continue as a highwayman with no trouble at all.

Well then, he would be a *good* bandit, like the great one of whom the cellmate in that jail months ago had told him, the storied Parra who robbed only the rich to pay the poor. Of course! A heroic bandit, whom all the peons would come to love. The very thought was exhilarating. It soothed the conscience, though little soothing was needed because he felt that he had actually committed no "moral" crime. The killing of Negrete was a needed thing; even his own friends had said so, eh! So, too, was the robbing of the rich *hacendados* a needed thing, if the money be given to the poor peons whom they enslaved.

"I will make a name for myself and soon even the despised Rurales will be my friends and not try to arrest me," he reasoned. "They are officers of the law, yes, but they are also mostly poor men like myself, they are not rich. They might even help me at times, if I first help them, if I be good to their families and their peon friends. They will come to respect the name of Teo Aran— No, I cannot use that name, of course, for I must hide, at least for a while. And the other names I have used, they too are known. What, then? What name for a friend of the poor people, a good *bandido*, who has to make his own way?"

Thus he day-dreamed as he rode, thus he built castles, thus he made and justified his plans. A new name, one to endure? He wished he could go now to his beloved Madrecita and consult her about it. Even though she would not approve all his plannings, she was gentle and kind, inspiring and wise. She would know a name. Teo knew something of his ancestry, because his beloved mother had told him. He knew, for example, that his paternal grandfather was named Jesus Villa. Jesus had an illegitimate son, Augustin, who because of the illegitimacy took his mother's name, Arango. Augustin Arango was Teo Arango's father. Thus but for the moral blemish on the older generation, Teo might have been Teo Villa.

"Villa is a good sounding name," he told himself on horseback. "But it would not do to use *Doroteo* Villa, or somebody might suspect. What, then?"

He considered many names: Juan, Enrico, Roberto, Guillermo, all the favorites of Mexico. Most were euphonious, and common enough. But they lacked—lacked what? Teo wasn't exactly sure. The "Villa" part had a good sound. He couldn't quite associate Jesus with it, or Juan, or Alberto, or Pedro, or any such. "Villa" needed a front name that was more—impressive? A bandit was not a common person, he should not have a common-sounding name, but should have something that was a pleasure to him and that would be remembered, eh? What, then?

The inherently romantic nature of the young man came up suddenly with Francisco. It sounded aristocratic. He mouthed it—"Francisco Villa." It was good. The nickname for Francisco was Pancho; Mexicans dearly love to make diminutives of their boy and girl names anyway, he knew, and often shorten an impressive name as a token of endearment. Could he, the bandit Villa of the future, some day be loved as "Pancho Villa"? Who knows? He smiled, enjoying the thought, the dreaming.

Good sense told him that he *was* just day-dreaming, but good sense also told him that he did truly need a new alias, and Francisco Villa would serve as well as any. It pleased the person who would use it, and it would be something to hide behind as need arose. He earnestly expected to make a need. The childhood hatred for rich ranchers who had beaten him, for all their kind who enslaved Mexico's peons, was not forgotten in the face of personal danger now. It was, rather, intensified, because they were a direct cause of that danger. He felt anew his possessive love for all poor workers. He dreamed grandly again of championing them, and knew that he would have their support. They would befriend him, help him to hide, cheer him on, protect him when need be. Well, then?

He could scarcely wait. He knew he must lie low for some months to escape his immediate pursuers, but he sensed that he could then begin to strike, and he knew—he *knew*, even now—that he would find loyal followers if he wanted them. It took no great imagination to envision a bandit band; a dozen maybe, or fifty, or a hundred. An army? He did not think of a military career. Oh to be sure, soldiers with their natty uniforms and stiff formality and guns and swords had fascinated the boy Doroteo Arango, but the dashing new-grown Francisco Villa was concerned more with individual freedom and action. Soldiers themselves were slaves, he had noted; they could rarely do as they pleased, but were at somebody's command. He, Teo—no, Francisco—would take *nobody's* commands henceforth. He would steal the best of horses, would strike suddenly and unexpectedly, would flee like the winds and disappear like the mirages. If other good men in time came to follow him, they must move as he moved.

He had reasoned himself into a feeling of security, leaping ahead with plans, giving real life to the strength that he ultimately meant to have. Thus he became incautious within a few days after his escape, and dared to accost a casual acquaintance he chanced to see out hunting. This one, named Pablo Martinez, was a peon even as Teo Arango had been, and so should have been sympathetic. But alas, Pablo knew of the rewards now offered for the young outlaw. Barely two days after their pleasant meeting, Francisco Villa was asleep in deep grass when a voice awoke him. As had happened before while hiding, he looked up into the muzzles of guns. This time there were not three, but seven.

He stood up slowly, and in the process he began cursing. When he was erect, his huge chest bulging, his thick hair in ebony whirlpools, his tanned face boyish but stern and wrathful, he swore with a passionate fury at the man by whom he had been betrayed, then turned on his captors. They might have shot him down, indeed would have been justified in so doing. Somehow they were much too impressed. Here was no sniveling criminal begging for mercy, here was a strikingly handsome and proud young man. He was bigger in body than any of them, he stood with his feet wide apart and his fists on his hips, staring straight into their eyes and cursing them fiercely. They waited in astonishment akin to hypnotism until he was done. Suddenly he seemed to have had the release of it, seemed ready to face what must be faced—a new situation. Strangely enough, he felt no fear; perhaps that is why he showed none. He felt only anger, at the Judas, at them, at himself for carelessness. Having expressed it, he was alert to the next need. And so all at once his voice changed and he actually grinned at them.

"Why so many guns, my friends?" he asked. "Can't you see I am unarmed?"

Why, indeed? These men had no reply, they had simply ordered him to surrender. He moved around as if one of them now, completely at ease, casually defiant of their cocked rifles.

"I have surrendered, so stop showing off," he continued. "You have a job to do, that I understand. But we can be friends. We are from the same neighborhood, so why be enemies? You have traveled hard, you have not eaten for hours, maybe; no more have I. I say let's roast some corn, have a meal and rest, then you may take me wherever you will."

He saw his captors relax a trifle; some lowered their guns. After all he was unarmed, as he said, and they were seven strong. Besides—he was a likable man, eh?

Their leader, Felix Sarinana, was convinced. "Why not?" he smiled in return. "Men, we certainly can't be afraid of this poor guy. Let's roast the corn, eat with him, and tomorrow take him to San Juan del Rio. It's a long distance, you know."

As usual, some hard-to-convince member of the posse expressed fear. This one insisted that they had best take no chances, that the prisoner was dangerous, desperate, unafraid. Francisco studied him intently and reacted on instinct.

"Are *you* afraid, my friend?" he demanded, walking boldly up to that one. "You, with six armed compadres? Maybe you should have stayed at home, maybe you should roost with the chickens."

The others all laughed. Ridicule is a potent weapon.

"Maybe you don't care for what I did, eh? What I did was shoot down the cowardly dog who lured my little sister into his bed and left her with child. She is a peon, a poor person like yourself, and like I was, and all of us. For having stood up against Don Augustin Negrete who is the oppressor of us all, you would have me boiled in tar, maybe, before being shot at sunrise. Hah!"

His contempt was powerful and it had its effect. Sarinana spat into the grass around them and said, "He is right. I only wish—" He shrugged it off. "We have orders, we have no choice. But of a surety we can eat before we return. Now, where do we get the corn?"

Down slope not more than half a mile away was a field of the corn with ears ripe for eating; fresh, juicy-sweet ears, delectable even if eaten raw, but better if roasted in their shucks in hot ashes. This field in fact accounted for Francisco's presence in the area; he had eaten a meal from it already, and planned to steal still more. Sarinana sent two to cut corn for all and two more to gather firewood. That left an adequate three to guard Francisco Villa—more than enough, as he himself said. He and these three moved a few rods to the top of a little bluff over a stream. The water was some thirty feet below, and the rocky top of the escarpment here provided an excellent place to cook, away from the grass which was dry and might be fired. Young Pancho himself suggested the move—but in him was a further reason, about which he said nothing.

While the four men waited here he talked more, in the same vein as before. Immediately he observed that they were interested. This fact encouraged him. Words? He had no education, no schooling. He could not even read and write. Could it be that he, the new Pancho Villa, was an influence with words as well as guns? He recalled that several haughty and "unapproachable" young women had suddenly been influenced by his charm. His own mother, his brothers and sisters, his employers, his associates almost everywhere, had seemed unconsciously to look *up* to him, accepting his instinctive leadership in things large and small. And had he not become a minor boss in the ranch work without anyone's quite realizing it? Had he not found jobs quickly no matter where he applied in city or town? He had done nothing but ask, nothing but talk and look into their eyes. And so now on the rock cliff above the stream he abruptly knew for a certainty that words as well as guns were weapons. He began using them more avidly than ever. He told, with all the fervor he could muster, *why* he wanted to champion the poor people's cause. The sheer emotional intensity of him somehow came through, and his listener-captors were obviously impressed. He saw, after a few moments, that they were softening, becoming unwatchful, unalert. It was the moment he had played for.

"I have to urinate," said he, slowly standing, stretching. Then he casually started as if to go behind a nearby bush. What they did not guess, but what he had known when he lured them up here, was that he had slept last night behind that bush, a thick scrub oak. His blanket was still there on the ground—and under it, a pistol.

In sudden open-mouthed astonishment they beheld him when he jumped back from behind the bush. He was smiling broadly, white teeth gleaming, eyes flashing in excitement.

"I should leave your flesh here for the buzzards that would quickly gather," said he, impressively. "But as I told you, I am not who you thought I was. I am not your enemy, but your friend. I am a friend of all our kind, never forget. For a few miserable pesos reward you would have taken me in to be executed. Yet I will not kill you, as I should. I give you more time to think about all that I have said. And so if you would live, do exactly as I say—*roll off that cliff! Now! Down into the stream!*" They did not protest. The muzzle of his pistol was a fearful thing. He heard three splashes down below, then he turned and ran. There was something else they had not known—that his fine horse, saddled, with rifle in scabbard, was tethered just around the next clump of trees.

5

Far back in the Sierra Gamon of Mexico are dozens of canyons which have been visited by no human beings for perhaps a hundred years, if ever. The harsh rock mountains there suggest that time is not as old as human beings think it is; that only yesterday the earth retched then vomited from its fiery bowels, and that barely enough centuries have sped by to complete the cooling of the saw-toothed peaks, and grind down enough powdery soil to support vegetation.

Francisco Villa, now "Pancho" in his own mind, rode into an area here which he named Hell's Canyon. Mephistopheles himself sat yonder two hundred feet high yet dwarfed by black cubistic pyramids and castles tossed in hellish disarray. Pancho found a spot where a whole cliff had tilted, waited perhaps two million years, then toppled completely, a segment of it falling across two great boulders and remaining intact. Thus it was a natural auditorium with space enough to house a troop of cavalry. Pancho had to spur his horse to make it enter, for the animal beheld the dark interior with misgivings, looked wide-eyed at it, snorted, tried to turn back. When they were safely under the great rock roof, Pancho dismounted and looked carefully around. In the back of the room he found a pile of bones and recognized them as remains of animals.

"Some lioness has made her lair here," he tlod himself, "and has brought in fawns and calves and other food for her cubs." Undoubtedly his horse had caught the scent of lion, hence stood there trembling.

Well then, so protected a lair would serve a man, too; it would make a hidden home. He dismounted, unsaddled his tired horse, and staked it outside in lush grass. He knew he was at least ten miles from any human habitation, but he also knew that a good clear stream rolled and tumbled not a hundred yards away. And best thing—he had ridden into the canyon behind twelve head of cattle. An expert cowboy, he had found it easy to cut the twelve from a herd far down country and drive them into the

Sierra. He had a bag of salt, he had a larger bag of corn meal, he had a heavy cake of mescal meat—the sweet, highly nourishing, condensed "candy" of the Indians, made from the chopped and baked leaves of the century plant. What more could a man ask? He had food enough for months of luxury living.

The cattle already were grazing on the canyon floor, and with the virgin grass and water at hand he knew they would stay nearby. So now he could take his ease, and this he did; he found a "bedroom" inside the great rocky chamber back under an attic-like slope, and there he piled armloads of the tall, dried grass he was able to gather. Within the hour he had a mattress such as he had rarely enjoyed in the haunts of man. Rolled in his blankets on this hay, he lay down to get the rest that was long past due him. Any man, however strong and energetic, must ultimately have a chance to restore.

He was up at dawn, and after breakfast he shot the fattest of the beeves. He had a belt knife, its blade eight inches long. This he stuck with a quick, powerful thrust into the animal's throat, then stood back to let the blood gush. With lariat rope tied to a back foot and his saddled horse to pull it over a tree limb, he swung the animal up for gutting. All the way he worked with a happy proficiency, humming a little, talking now and then to his horse as any lonely cowboy does.

"You are a grass eater, *caballo*," he said. "Thus you are out of luck, eh? You do not know what is good. Now if you ate meat I would give you the lights and the livers and maybe a slice of roast. You are lucky I do not eat you, too, eh? You, *caballo mio*, you hammer-headed devil, what good are you, eh?" It was jovial, friendly fellowship and it occupied the mind while the hands moved fast.

Pancho carried sections from the hanging carcass to a nearby stone of table height and on this began his stripping. With deft strokes he cut the flesh into strings about an inch thick and six to twelve inches long, and draped these over dead tree limbs that he gathered and placed upright in the bright sun. One mesquite some six feet tall had died. This he festooned with the red strips so that it looked like a Yankee Christmas Tree he remembered seeing in a magazine picture. He stood off to admire it, even moving some of the strips for better esthetic effect. It pleased him to realize that he could take time from hard, bloody, "un-artistic" work to give attention to beauty.

The stripping and the hanging up and the resting and the cleaning of the butcher area took all of that day, but it was a good day and in the process he had much time for reflection. He slept as contentedly as he had ever known himself to sleep, for he felt secure from captors and he had been adding to his life plans. Best thing immediately, he knew, was just to stay out of sight. He was far now from those seven men who had last captured him, and he had won some favor in their sight anyway, he believed. For one thing, he had not killed their leader and the other two from whom he had escaped. What is a dive into water, when life itself had been hanging by a hair? They would be grateful to him. They would remember his talk of championing the peons.

So, now, he set in for weeks of work as a butcher. Those twelve cattle became jerked meat. The strips turned dark and hard in four or five days of the intense sunshine. From the hides he fashioned balloon-like containers which dried in the sun to become stronger than any baskets, and he sewed the jerked meat into these with rawhide strings. One by one he swung these inside his cave so that no bear or other thieving animal could get at them. When he looked at that finished storehouse it was with satisfaction. The meat represented wealth, he knew. It was food for himself to last out a year if need be. More important, it was merchandise which could be bartered or sold.

One day after two months had passed, he loaded two of the biggest bags of meat back of his saddle and ventured out. He had been scouting the country meanwhile. About twelve miles distant he had spotted men cutting trees in a forest. These would want food, perhaps; lumberjacks were eternally hungry. He had grown considerable hair on his face by now, and his head hair was long, scraggly, untidy. He looked exactly as he wished to look—like an average poverty-ridden peon. He concealed the horse when near the lumberjacks' camp.

The meeting was altogether pleasant. "My name is Pancho Villa," said he, head bowed as if in humility when they asked him. "I have some jerked meat to sell."

"Pancho Villa, hah?" one answered. "I have heard of him, but you do not look like him. Pancho Villa was a bandit in the olden days."

Young Pancho tried not to show his surprise. "I did not know him, señor. I have not heard of him before. He is dead now?"

"Long since. *You* are no bandit, hey?" And he laughed big with the other men. "We have no money to buy meat. It is probably burro or horse anyway."

"It is the finest beef!"

"Hah! You are proud. It is good, my friend. Let me sample it, eh?"

The sampling was satisfactory. Pancho had salted just enough of it, in the making, for superb taste, though he wasted no salt on the bulk of it. "You can bring more?" they asked.

"Eight more sacks."

"What can we trade you?"

In the end he had from them a fine stock of ammunition. It would fit his pistol and his rifle, and it was what he needed most. Another blanket was added, and an item or two of clothing. They even offered him a job, noting what a powerful figure of a man he was, and the wage was more than satisfactory. But he pretended no interest and, by a circuitous route lest he be spied on, went on back to his lair.

Another month passed before he dared come out again. Sheer loneliness drove him. He had practiced shooting until his marksmanship was virtually perfect, his speed with rifle or pistol unbelievable. He had made and re-made many plans, and while he had expected to stay hidden for at least a year, boredom took over, boredom and a yearning for girls. The glands within him made insistent demand, and he had insufficient work to take his mind off this need. So, he ventured by night to the farm called San Isabel de Berros, where he had friends. First person he recognized there was one who could hardly have been more appropriate, to his thinking. It was Lucretia Maldonado, a comely señorita, and she was carrying table scraps to a pig pen when he spoke from some bushes nearby.

"Teo!" she exclaimed. "You frightened me!"

"Sh-h-h-h-h! I am not Teo any more. I am Pancho Villa."

"Oh? How is that? I have known you for—"

"Hush, and come here. Come to me, Lucretia. I want to kiss you."

50

"But, *Teo!*"

He already had her in his arms and next moment he was carrying her bodily into the shrubbery from which he had come. There he stood her on her feet a moment and kissed her long and hard. When he felt her responding, he knew he could have what he craved.

The meeting took less than half an hour, after which Pancho went to the home of a friend named Jesus Alday. He wanted news, if any; he wanted companionship, he wanted to sit and talk.

"You have become famous, Teo, *seguro si,*" said Jesus, heartily.

"I am not Teo Arango, I am Pancho Villa. You understand? That Arango is dead forever. He was killed in an accident, drowned in a flood, let us say. You will tell of it, friend Jesus? You will remember that Doroteo Arango who shot Negrete is dead, alas, for protecting his sister. But Pancho Villa—not the old bandit of years ago, but a new one who is a friend of all Mexicans who work and are oppressed—he is very much alive. You understand me, Jesus? *¿Sabe usted?*"

The romantic thought appealed to Jesus. Yes indeed he understood. It was a thing to meditate on, eh? A something to occupy the mind as one bent over his plow or hoe for endless hours. A hope and a promise to discuss in the dust-laden twilight or under the moon after day's work was ended and men had gathered for mutual comfort. Tell me more, friend Teo—no, friend *Pancho,* I mean. Pancho Villa, a good name, a name to remember.

"There is little more to tell, as yet. But there will be more, Jesus, this I promise. I have plans."

"What kind of plans?"

"Good plans. One of these nights—who knows when—I will tap on your window and whisper loudly—'*Jesus, it is time!*'"

The man was all a-tingle with excitement. "You will, Pancho? And what will we do? Tell me, man!"

"Never mind. You just be ready. And you tell others, a select few. Not in loud speeches, my friend. Not for women to hear, not for gossips. This is *man's* work. Jesus, you have a rifle, a pistol, a knife?"

"I will get them. I swear it."

"Good. And get ammunition. Hide them where they can't be taken away from you but where you can find them quickly. Then be ready. One night you will get the message that Pancho calls. You will have a good horse, saddle, and bridle spotted, and a blanket and some food maybe. Tell no one, just come to meet me where the message will say.

With that the young man was gone, leaving Jesus Alday staring after him, mouth open, wide-eyed. Before he was out of sight, though, Jesus ran to catch him. "Pancho!" he murmured guardedly. "Come with me. I will introduce you to two friends who think as you do."

"Friends? You are sure, Jesus?"

"I am sure. They are—they—they are already acting, Pancho. They do things you will like."

"I will meet them. But if there is any trick—Jesus, I can shoot six beans off a rock in three seconds, from the hip. I am not boasting. I have practiced long. You understand?" He had gripped the man's shoulders fiercely, shaking him a little.

"I understand, Pancho. There is no trick. You will see."

The meeting was arranged for next day. When it took place, young Pancho himself was the one to be awed. Quite unexpectedly he came face to face with two men in their thirties, arrogant, fierce of countenance, strong, and well armed. One was introduced as Refugio Alvarado. "And this, Pancho," said Jesus Alday, removing his big straw sombrero in obvious respect, "is El Señor Ignacio Parra."

Young Pancho could not hide his surprise, but he looked straight at the man. With no fear, he refused to be stared down. Finally he smiled, feeling he could at least be friendly. Parra. The name was powerful. It was the one he had first learned while a prisoner in jail, the name of a bandit almost legendary, the very one on which he himself had built his planning. Ignacio Parra, the bandit who robbed the rich to help the poor, so people said.

"This kid, this brat, is the one you say is so tough?" Parra asked Jesus Alday now.

"He is very strong, señor. He is brave."

"That we shall see." Then he turned to Pancho again. "You want to come along with us, sonny? You want to ride with Parra?"

52

"Yes."

"Yes, *sir*, sonny. Say it!" His eyes squinted a warning at Pancho. Pancho stared back at him hard, but remained silent.

"Well?" demanded Parra.

"*Yes!*" Pancho repeated, and waited. After a moment—"I say *yes*, I want to ride with you, if you think I can be of any help. Yes."

Another ageless pause followed. Then Ignacio Parra broke into a big grin and extended his hand. "You will ride with us. Meet us here at sundown. We move toward the Hacienda de la Soledad. You realize, of course, that I ought to have killed you a moment ago; that I could easily have done so."

"I do not. I would have killed you first. I am very fast on the draw, and I can shoot better than any man I ever saw. I am not boasting."

"We are not enemies, young fellow. You will have a chance to prove what you say, but let us not take it out on one another, eh? There are plenty who will be enemies of us both."

The troop of thieves camped next night near the village of Tejame, a few miles from the Concha farms. Shortly before darkness fell, Parra came to Pancho.

"Sonny boy, the only thing we know how to do is steal and kill. Now there at the Concha is a herd of mules. They will be your test. Maybe you never herded any animals, eh? We will see what you can do. If you make a lot of noise you may have to prove how well you shoot. If you don't come back with the mules, you will surely have to prove it—to me."

The bandit chieftain lay down on his bed of blankets, and a pretty mistress came to sit beside him, holding a guitar. Young Pancho watched them. He understood. A man needs a woman, often. Parra carried his along. She began to strum softly and presently she was crooning. He edged away, lest he appear too bold now, but he stayed near enough to listen. Her voice haunted him in the gathering shadows of evening. The campfire was friendly. A covey of birds swooped low, saw the fire and, in perfect military precision, swerved upward in a U-turn to settle on a nearby tree. Pancho thought the woman's voice was like that of Sonoran doves. It penetrated deep into him and revived an intense longing for a woman of his own.

At 11 p.m. Pancho Villa came back to the Parra camp and the bandit leader himself greeted him, half smiling. "Well now, it's my sonny boy! How goes it, eh? You are ready to go after the mules?"

Pancho spat in the grass. "The mules, señor, are waiting just outside our camp."

It was true. With no fanfare, no shooting, no trouble, the Pancho Villa who had been reared in ranch work had simply stolen the herd, driving them into a nearby area, keeping them calm. Parra walked out to see, then broke into genial cursing. "And just when I was ready for sleep," he growled, in mock anger. "Sonny, you served too well. Now we will have to break camp and get out of here, for we will surely be attacked if we don't. But please don't think I am angry."

Two days later Ignacio Parra called Pancho to his tent in another camp, miles away. With no ceremony he held out a roll of bills to the young man. "This money is yours," said he. "We sold those mules to Don Ramon, another farmer friend of mine. This is your share."

Pancho counted it. He was holding, unbelievably, more than three thousand pesos. Never before in his life had he even seen so much money, let alone owned it. It was a fortune. It was earned in barely two hours work, between nine and eleven o'clock one evening. If banditry paid such rewards as this—!

He would buy new and better clothes, which he sadly needed.

He would buy a new and better horse, with a good saddle.

He would buy another fine pistol, for a bandit needs two.

One by one he enumerated to himself the things he would get with this fortune. Then suddenly he remembered his mother, and that in turn refocused his attention on his ideals. Banditry? For selfish advantage? Not he. He was to be Pancho Villa who robbed the rich to help the poor, not just to amass a personal fortune and be all his life a fugitive from the law. True, any bandit would be a fugitive; but a good one would have endless friends, and the law would not be able to molest him much. Besides, he didn't want a personal fortune; actually didn't crave a lot of luxury, he assured himself. All a man needed—wasn't it?—was a good set of camp equipment, good guns, loyal followers. And, say, a girl who could play a guitar and sing with

54

him and comfort his groin. That would be luxury enough.

He told Ignacio Parra he would be gone for a few hours because he was going to visit his mother. She was a poor peon; the first of his loot could rightfully and happily go to her. And so it was. She was tearfully grateful, not only for assurance of his safety for which she had feared, but for the incredible bounty of money he put in her lap.

On that trip, too, he learned by tactful inquiry that the young man Doroteo Arango, who had shot the rancher Negrete several months ago, was now dead. They say he was shot by some soldiers. They say he was drowned in a flood. They say Don Augustin Negrete's men caught him, castrated him, then burned him in a fire. Well, no matter, he is dead, and that is that, eh my young friend Villa? He was about your age, they say.

Pancho avoided persons he knew even though his appearance was radically changed. He kept his hair cut and combed differently, he had a severe mustache, he walked erect with a studied stride, and he wore clothes no humble peon farmer-rancher could ever wear. The search had naturally ended; Doroteo Arango was dead indeed.

That day he was passing a bar room when he saw a beautiful black horse under a brand new saddle, hitched to a rail. With no preliminary scouting, in fact with no worry or qualms of any kind, Pancho quietly unhitched the animal and mounted it. Quickly it sensed his skill, his sure hand, as it stepped around the street there, properly guided by knees and heels and reins. The owner inside the bar heard him and ran out.

"Oyez! What you do there? That is my horse!"

Pancho didn't even bother to answer the man; he just heeled the horse's sides. They sped away with a flourish.

Hours later, Ignacio Parra and his associate Refugio admired the horse and saddle generously, than asked how much it had cost.

"Practically nothing," replied Pancho, sedately. "Just the trouble of mounting him and rescuing him from a drunkard who had forgotten him at the door of a bar."

The older bandits laughed uproariously, slapping their thighs and one another's shoulders, enjoying their recruit's daring.

55

"Ho!" exclaimed Parra. "It is a horse better than my own. I will take him, eh? For me to ride."

"If you do," quietly replied young Pancho, not smiling, "I will shoot you down. It was your idea that we be friends. I hope it has not changed, Señor Parra."

Parra laughed again. "It has not changed, sonny. I believe you mean what you say."

6

YOUNG PANCHO VILLA broke with Parra over an incident that, as Pancho decided later, seemed a triviality. Parra's band had taken yet another recruit into membership, a no-good killer named José Solis. One day the bandits were riding toward the town of Canatlan to slip in and buy ammunition, when they encountered a barefoot peon leading a burro laden with two big cartons.

"What's in the boxes, man?" demanded José Solis rudely.

The peon removed his hat and said, "Bread. For the Santa Isabel de Berros farm."

"*Bueno!* Then you will sell us a few loaves. We are hungry."

"I cannot sell it to you. It is not for sale."

"Then we'll take it."

"No!" The peon had dignity and courage. "Neither you nor any one else can tell me what to do with my belongings. I don't even know you."

With no further word or warning, Solis drew a pistol and fired two shots into the baker's body, killing him instantly. Then with his knife he cut into the boxes, took out a loaf and started eating. Presently he rode on. Not one of the other bandits, witnesses of the murder, took any of the bread. After a few moments Pancho Villa rode up to Parra.

"I'm leaving you," said he. "We have no right to murder a poor man just for bread."

Parra shrugged. "Pull out whenever you feel like it, sonny. This is a man's game."

56

"Man's game! It's a devil's game and I'm done with it."

"Careful you don't get what the baker got, kid."

"Just try it. Let Solis try it."

On horseback they faced one another, for a last time. Each had come to respect the other's iron nerve. Each knew the other was a good shot, and that of the two, Pancho was the better. Parra made no move. Young Villa faced him for a few moments then spurred, swung his horse, leaned low in the saddle to make a smaller target, and darted into dense shrubbery beside the road. Nobody shot at him, somewhat to his surprise. He never saw Ignacio Parra or any of Parra's band again.

When he felt safely out of reach of Parra's guns, he slowed his horse and started thinking. Once more, he realized, he was a lone bandit. He knew that Don Augustin Lopez Negrete would still be happy to see him arrested. But then, Doroteo Arango was "dead"; wherever he had made tactful inquiry the young man was reported killed. This at least was gratifying, he told himself now, smiling a bit. "Pancho Villa can operate safely," he spoke aloud to his horse. Then sagely added, "If he is careful, and stays at a distance."

By sundown that day he realized that he hadn't the stomach for more banditry at the moment. Loneliness, homesickness, craving for peace and love and quiet, assailed him again. Yet he had nowhere to go, no place to look for rest. He yearned for his Madrecita.

In his lonely camp that night he dreamed of her, of his home bed, of the mother's tenderness. All his life, he realized, it would be so; he would yearn for his childhood, stark though it had been. "Am I a weakling?" he asked himself there on his blanket in the wilds. "Am I not a grown man, able to take care of myself?"

He tried thus to bolster his spirits, and he failed. No man is ever fully grown, he finally realized, looking out at the Mexican stars. Every man clings to mother, either in fact or fancy, or both. It was clear to him now; he had seen it many times in others. It was why the church honored the Virgin Mother, eh? *Seguro si.* Right and proper, that was. The thought made him feel better; at least he was not alone in his "weakness" and yearning for home. It was common to all men.

He got up once and walked out a few steps to urinate. Stood on a rock and watched the stream catch the light of a waning moon. This amused him. He remembered that as a boy he and other boys sometimes held contests to see who could throw their streams the farthest out, and that he invariably won. He was still vaguely proud of that, and chuckled now at the memory of it. Once some girls had heard them laughing and had run to see what caused it. The other boys disappeared in embarrassment, but he had stood his ground and frankly answered their questions. The matter had intrigued them. They demanded a demonstration. By appointment, then, four hours later he had performed solo before a small but appreciative audience, setting a record of almost eight feet. This had given him enviable stature among the village children back there. And now the mature Pancho laughed out loud at the memory. It restored his spirits so that he lay down again and enjoyed a sound sleep.

Next dawn he started on a long journey into the State of Chihuahua, to the town of Parral. An unwonted confusion rode with him. His far-flung plans of a few weeks ago? He had not abandoned them but he had pushed them aside for the moment, and he studied other horizons. His inability to visit home was frustrating; he wasn't sure just what he would do. For want of anything more definitely in his plan, he simply got himself an honest, workaday job. It was in La Verde Mine and it paid a good wage. He didn't mind that the work was hard.

He stayed there longer than he had expected. He suffered a foot injury and a doctor ordered an amputation. He threatened to kill the doctor, gave himself to two peon women healers who with their primitive science of plasters and leaves cured the infection and saved the leg. He studied their methods—what kind of plasters, what herbs, to combat gangrene.

On recovery he was offered an even better job as overseer for a bunch of adobe brick layers, and from this made more money. One week his share of profits, granted by the contractor, amounted to almost two hundred pesos. Thus Pancho Villa might have lived the remainder of his days as a steadily prosperous, prosaic, hard-working, average—and forgotten—man. He felt tempted to do just that—and was angry at himself for it.

"Is your real name Pancho Villa?" a stranger asked him one day, after riding up to him on a horse.

"Of course," said Pancho, genuinely surprised, but frightened too.

"You look a lot like a description here of a man wanted in Durango. A murderer named Doroteo Arambula."

Arambula had been his mother's maiden name. Sometimes she was known as Micaela Arambula, as well as Arango for her late husband. Similarly, son Doroteo had sometimes been called by the Arambula name.

"Sorry I can't help you sir. If you want proof—" Pancho shrugged, bluffing hard.

"I'll get my own proof," the official said. "I'll inquire."

If he did inquire, Pancho never knew it. Before midnight the young man was far away. On his fine horse, in his expensive saddle, carrying his two pistols and his rifle and his belt knife, his blankets and packs of food, he was headed full speed once more for the Sierra Gamon. Pancho Villa, the lone bandit, had come alive again.

Riding back toward his hideout was as tedious a journey as he had ever made, and after twenty-four hours or so of it he grew so lonely that he fell once more to day dreaming. His old plans of being a Robin Hood sort of bandit (though it is doubtful if he ever heard of Robin Hood) were revived, reactivated, expanded. He would do more than just rob rich ranchers and give the loot to poor peons; he would also raid jails and free any innocent prisoners, such as he himself had been. He would swoop down on any dishonest, bribe-taking Rurales or other police, strip them of their uniforms and guns and badges, give them a firm warning and maybe a whipping. To help him do this he, of course, would have to select capable, fearless henchmen, members of Pancho Villa's band. He knew—somehow he *knew*—that he could readily recruit them, though he was still young. He had already demonstrated that ability for glamorous leadership.

"Well then," he mused, riding cross country toward the west, "I must be prepared for my followers. They can bring most of what they will need, such as a horse, saddle, bridle, blanket, perhaps even guns. But few can get ammunition. I must build up a supply of that."

59

He swung his horse back toward the Santa Isabel de Berros farm, for two reasons; he would stop near there at a store whose proprietor he knew to be friendly to him and get all the cartridges he could carry, and he would visit his beloved Madrecita, the mother for whose smile he always yearned. He had one pleasant surprise just before reaching the farm. By chance there he came face to face with his own brother.

"Hipolito!" he cried.

For a long moment Hipolito did not recognize him. Pancho's new bearing, new clothes, new mustache, and generally changed appearance, were effective disguises. But the voice revealed him when he spoke again. The brothers flew to each other's arms as girls would have done.

"But I have bad news," Hipolito reported, after their greeting.

Pancho's face clouded and he was instantly alert. "They are after me? They know I am somewhere near?"

"No such thing. My brother, you are dead! Everybody thinks you are dead."

"Maybe Don Augustin does not. He has offered many rewards for me. Even in Parral a man was trying to learn if my name was Doroteo Arambula. He had an old paper, offering a reward."

"What of that? An *old* paper. But that is not what I mean. Teo, our mother is very sick. She may die."

So that was the bad news. Pancho was saddened indeed. He demanded every crumb of information, though he got little. She had taken ill unaccountably. A healing woman had been called, a Wise Woman. This one had sat by the Madrecita for long hours, mumbling, then she had placed an egg on the sick woman's abdomen, leaned her own face against it and talked some more. "Come out of the bowels," she had commanded the sickness. "Come out forever. Come out and into the egg." She had then placed the egg under a little earthen pot in the sick woman's bed and said that the illness would be gone tomorrow. When tomorrow came, the egg had turned black and the healing woman said the blackness was the sickness, now taken away. But the Madrecita—"She was sicker than before, my brother," said Hipolito, his face reflecting his sorrow. "The healing woman still works with her, but I—I—Teo, I am afraid she will die."

"Do not call me Teo," the big brother murmured. "No one

must know that I live. I must be extremely careful. But go to our mother and comfort her. If she can hear you when you are alone with her, say that I shall come to her tomorrow night. Beg her to be strong, Hipolito; to pray to the good Virgin and the saints as she did for us, eh? You can pray, Hipolito?"

"I can pray. Of a certainty. Any one can pray."

"Then pray."

"And you?" He looked up at the bigger young man.

"Praying, I do not understand. But you pray. I order you to. And I will come with money and comfort."

He left the brother then, and went off to make his concealed camp for the night. After eating he went cautiously back to the village where his mother, brothers, and sisters had their home, studying every detail from concealment. It wouldn't do to be recognized now. That night he slept little, and all next day he remained cautious, staying at a distance, watching, waiting for his chance. Finally he decided that the safest way to enter the little community where the "dead" Teo Arango had been well known would be the boldest one. If he crept in, anybody might wonder. If he moved in as if he were completely unafraid, a man going about his own business whatever it might be, nobody would suspect. Perhaps they would think he was a doctor. Had not his own brother Hipolito failed to recognize him before he spoke? Certainly. Well then. Thus Pancho reasoned with himself.

In the late twilight he tied his horse a hundred yards from his mother's hut, loosened the two pistols in his belt, and walked directly toward her place. At once he saw a dozen or so adults outside, motionless, standing. This was to be expected; friends would of course call after supper to inquire about her condition, and would linger to show their concern and respect. But then— through the open door he caught the gleam of two lighted candles.

"She is already dead!" he whispered, in sudden horror.

It was true. The young Pancho Villa, her oldest son, moved very slowly now. When he came closer the people outside saw him, though if they recognized him they made no sign. They parted so that he could enter. Presently he was staring at the one woman who had meant most to him, the only one who had ever been kind to him, the face of her being now in its last repose. Next moment he was on one knee beside her, his head on his other knee and her hand in his. He was sobbing as only a strong man can at the bier of his mother.

The sobbing ceased to wrack him presently, but he continued to stay there head on knee, eyes closed. By rights he should have kept his wake in peace. Dawn should have found him exhausted but calmer, ready then to bear her to her grave. But no. Not for Pancho Villa.

Some time before midnight he was shocked out of his grief by the unmistakeable overtones of danger. It began as a sudden rumble of masculine voices just outside the door. Pancho's head lifted, the strain on his emotions still showing. His face turned in inquiry.

"That's him, all right!" a voice said. "We've got him. Come out, Arango. With your hands high!"

One window of the room was open and it was nearest at hand. Pancho literally dived through it. Nobody shot into the room but he had barely hit the hard ground outside before he heard the crack of pistols.

His would-be captors had not planned nor acted well; or perhaps they simply had no knowledge of the new Pancho Villa. Left to flee unhindered, he could have made it to his horse and dashed away with no further horror to disturb the sacred scene of his mother's dying. But when some hasty fool dared shoot at the shadowy form of Pancho Villa his own two guns went into action. He took no aim, did not need to. He never even lost stride in his running save to swing around and fire with incredible rapidity. Four or five men were left bleeding and two were dead when the excited little crowd heard the fugitive's horse racing off in the distance.

Because nobody here had thought to bring horses and none could be had for a while, no pursuit was possible. For one thing, who wanted to chase a young man of such hellish accuracy with guns? Who would brave him next time they came onto his hiding place? Best forget him, at least for now; best forget the reward while burying the dead. By sunrise, moreover, a definite anger had spread through the other peons of the area; an anger that said the Judases who had recognized and betrayed the

62

young man should themselves be hanged. It would be best, yes, to forget about pursuit.

Days later, in his secret lair in the Sierra Gamon, Pancho Villa awoke one morning and went out to greet the sun. He stood looking at it almost worshipfully; reared closed to the earth, he had often felt a reverence for the sun. He stood there with feet spread wide, hands on hips, bareheaded, chin high. It came to him then and there that he was, at long last, grown. His mother, his beloved mother, was gone; he was of necessity completely on his own.

Pancho Villa sensed that a new chapter in his life, whatever of good or bad it might hold for him, was about to begin.

7

TONIGHT the moon swam like a dolphin. Even without looking up Pancho could follow its diving over and under and through the cloud waves, for the shadows it cast were flowing around him, giving soundless life to all the earth. This was good, he sensed; it was more than beautiful, it served as camouflage. One man walking alone into a rural village became just another of the myriad spirit forms now holding carnival.

Thus he arrived unseen at the adobe hut of a man he knew by name and temperament. He avoided going to the front, for it faced the street, but he moved silently to a side window and tapped.

"Jesus!" he called, softly.

An answer came at once—"¿Quien es?"

"Do not be afraid, Jesus. It is I. Your friend."

"Who?" the demand was louder.

"Sh-h-h-h! Do not wake any one. Come outside. Quietly."

In a moment the back door opened and there stood Jesus Alday clad only in dingy shorts. He held a pistol. "Come no closer," he warned, "until I see who you are."

"My friend, if I had meant to kill you I could have done so before now. You do not recognize me?"

"Pancho!"

"*¡Seguro si!*"

They embraced each other like women. Jesus stuck his gun under the belt of his shorts then grabbed Pancho's shoulders in affection. "It is time?" he demanded. "You have come for us? Now?"

This surprised Pancho, and delighted him.

"You remembered! Yes, Jesus, it is time. Now. When can you join me?"

"At once! Tonight! I have nearly twenty men ready!"

Pancho hugged his friend again, touched by the unexpected loyalty.

"I will dress and go spread the word. We have guns and provisions hidden, as you said. We have been hearing of you, Pancho. Hearing much. Most of us have been whipped again and again by the rich ones. It is a hell, I tell you, to be poor!"

"Yes, but we do not talk that now. We organize. Jesus, you know where the ancient ruin is, the rock walls that were a fortress on a hill."

"Of course. As children we—"

"Well then. It is four miles from here. Nobody, nothing, lives near it. Few people ever go there, eh? But there is a spring of water, and grass."

"We meet you there?"

"Yes." He looked toward the scudding clouds. "The moon will drop out of sight shortly before the sun shows. About then, I will meet you there. I have food. It is good, eh?"

"Ah, my Pancho! Go, now. Before some Judas spies you as before. I will spread the word!"

Pancho melted into the dancing shadows as silently as he had come. He felt elated. He hadn't been sure how much to expect of Jesus, and had found enthusiasm. It gave him renewed life. He hurried to his waiting horse.

The ride to his next point of call was three miles, so he spurred to a run over the plains and rolling hills, becoming a black centaur that must have startled lesser, more ethereal forms. If he was seen by mortal eye he never knew it. After the first mile some cattle lifted their rumps, climbed laboriously to four feet and snorted at him, debating whether to stampede. Before their slow minds could decide, he was already a faint echo in the distance.

A coyote on a ridge studied him, then disdainfully howled once and loped away. Two bats flew low, perhaps out of curiosity, before they too swerved on about their haunting or their hunting. Altogether it was a zestful, beautiful ride, even the horse enjoying it. The fine animal was puffing only gently when Pancho pulled up to creep quietly to another cluster of miserable peon homes.

This time he called at the house of Antonio Lares, and their conversation was much as before. Lares' wife came outside. He went to her at once. "Señora," he warned, "it is I, Pancho Villa. Nothing is to be said. *You understand?*"

"You are not to fear me, Teo."

"*Pancho!*"

"Pancho, *si*. I am your friend. All of us are your friends here. I have saved some money to help you. I bring it to you now." She held a little bag to him. Touched anew, he squeezed the coins, knowing they were few but precious, knowing the sacrifice they represented. He leaned impulsively to kiss her forehead. "Dios!" he murmured his surprise and gratitude. "You are good. You are generous and kind, señora. But here—" He reached into his own pocket for two golden coins worth several times what her bag held, and put all back into her work-hardened hands. "Loyalty we need. Money, no. We will get money to give to *you*. It is our mission. You understand? Thank you from my heart, but keep this. And there will be more."

He told Antonio where to meet him, then he was gone again. Before the moon had slanted downhill more than half way to the western peaks, he had made four other quiet, dramatic calls. In each case his reception was the same. Excitement. Eagerness. A whispered blessing. Offers of food, money, prayers. In each poverty-ridden home he left his own blessing and a coin, and vanished as romantically as he had arrived. Finally he raced to be ahead of his friends at the rendezvous.

When they arrived at the ancient hilltop ruin they saw no sign of Pancho. Their horses had been staked to rest and graze in the flats below, as he had indicated, and now on the hilltop they looked for him far and near. They were not an imposing group. They were poor indeed, most being barefoot, but each had a gun and each clutched some kind of bag with his few supplies. All but two wore great straw sombreros, the olden

65

badge of the peon. Practically all of them wore overalls, that most ubiquitous of garments. The chest bib was the only protection most of the men had above the waist, but they were accustomed to working bare-armed and rather enjoyed the freedom of it. In front, hip, and side pockets were such knives and cartridges as the men had been able to buy or steal.

Nearly forty had gathered in the pre-dawn before much talking began, and it was one named Bernabe who first spoke loudly. "I believe we are fools," said he. "We have waited long and I am cold. It is dark here, and I have no food. If that Pancho thinks—"

Instantly there was an outburst; a threatening but guarded condemnation of Bernabe from several trying to speak at once. Nobody could see another's face clearly, but some knew others by sound of voice. The angry ones subsided, then a soft chuckling was heard and a man dressed in sombrero and overalls like the others stepped quietly out of the group.

"You can go, Bernabe," this one said quietly. "I am already done with you."

"Pancho!"

Several exclaimed it. He had been in their very midst, minus his fine charro costume.

"I said you can go, Bernabe. Now I say you had *better* go, damn you. And fast! In ten seconds I shall start shooting at you."

Bernabe was intelligent enough, Pancho observed, to know that his life hung by a hair. He leaped, hit running, and was out of sight when Pancho boomed "Ten!" Pancho did not shoot, he merely laughed, enjoying the incident. It was a trick he now resolved to use again if test was needed; and in fact, did use it many times in months to come.

He had a definite plan, he told his loyal ones. He felt their warmth of friendship as he talked. They asked few questions; only enough to understand their roles clearly. The conspiratorial air was like that he had sometimes felt as a small boy playing with friends, Pancho recalled. It stimulated him, gave him great confidence and poise, as he moved about recruiting still more followers.

Thus four dawns later at the Rancho del Rio, a relatively small spread in the south of Chihuahua, servants were preparing breakfast and overseers were issuing their work orders for the day. These proceedings were halted abruptly by the unseemly sound, at this hour, of many horsemen approaching. The men and women in the barnyard turned to look. Pancho, riding hard and enjoying it, led his group into the home area and reined up with a flourish. He heard the nearly one hundred men behind him stop their horses, and felt their mass strength somehow flow into him. This was new and heady experience. He saw an arrogant looking man leave the ranch house and walk toward him.

"What is this?" that one demanded. "Who are you?"

Pancho smiled broadly, showing white teeth. "If you are the owner here, señor, direct your servants to prepare food for us at once. Then you and your family get out. Start walking away from the ranch. And do not come back if you value your lives."

The man afoot glared up at him in shock. "What do you mean? I am Don Fabian Armendariz!"

Pancho nodded, still smiling, but with menace now. He was alert as he swung down from his saddle.

"*Get out!*" Pancho shouted it, pointing away from the ranch.

Don Fabian, more courageous than wise, drew a dagger from his belt. Pancho felt no fear. In one lightning-like motion he grabbed the older man, wrested the weapon from him, then threw him so forcefully into the dirt that he lay there stunned, and finally tossed the dagger on top of him.

"You would stab Pancho Villa, ha!" Pancho felt the eyes of men upon him, knew the zest of being an actor, center stage.

Across the courtyard his eye caught a movement; another man afoot had made sudden motion as if to draw a pistol. He never got it unholstered. Pancho's own beautiful gun—the left-hand one at that—spoke twice in quick succession. He hadn't even given it thought, the move had been involuntary. He saw the other man fall, sensed that he was unconscious even before he plopped to the ground.

That morning on the rancho he and his men ate well. The handsome young leader beheld, with satisfaction, his impact on the servants here. They were secretly delighted to feed his band. Seven of them asked to join him, and were welcomed. He went among all the servants greeting them, even kissing the women and hugging the older ones.

67

"You are free!" he exclaimed. "You are no longer slaves. Pancho Villa promises that. Help us now to free others like you. Remember, I was one of your kind, I too was a slave."

The band gathered priceless food, ammunition, clothing, money, even souvenirs. The raid on Rancho del Rio had been astonishingly easy. But then, as Pancho expansively asked one of his lieutenants, what chance had any ranch against nearly one hundred armed, well-disciplined men fighting God's battle? Truly Pancho was savoring his new power.

When he led them away before sundown, instinct told him that he had begun an indelible legend. He had seen life from the ranch folk's point of view. Now he realized that news of the raid would spread with the speed that only such news can show; from plowman to sheep herder; from cowboy to cowboy, to footman on the road laboring under his burden of pottery, to the driver of an ox cart wheeling to the nearest town, to this one and that one in ever-mounting excitement. He spoke of all this in elation to the compadres now riding beside him.

"It is good, *amigos*," said he, in high spirits. "Do you know why? It is because *we have left much food, clothing and money in every worker's home!* Can you see what that means? Poor people can hold up their heads. With bellies full, they can feel like *men!*"

Pancho literally shouted, an orator without realizing it. His horse, startled, cocked an eye back at him then galloped on without breaking rhythm. Pancho molded to him in perfect grace. The rider at his side nodded emphatic agreement, murmured respectfully "*Si, si, Pancho, es bueno*." Again the vigorous young leader felt the support thundering behind him, horsemen and fighters blending their strength into his own. He turned in his stirrups, lifted a hand in salute. A cheer came instantly, involuntarily. Pancho Villa had never felt so good in all his life.

Success breeds success; instinct, not experience, told him that. So, within thirty days he had fearlessly swooped down on three other ranches scattered about the State of Chihuahua, and sure enough the rule held. At no point was the opposition more than token; one or two men might shoot at the Villistas, and die in the instant for their folly.

"It is a shame to kill good men," Pancho mentioned once, and meant it. "But what can we do?" He shrugged, excusing himself with the age-old alibi of self-defense. He had instructed his followers to shoot only if need be, but then to shoot fast and true. They did precisely that. He realized again and again that he was no outlaw to the peons on those ranches; he was a liberator.

So then, on a day in autumn he confidently led his men on their most exciting adventure to date, a truly bold move. He planned it carefully, even gleefully, talking with half a dozen henchmen from his band, finally placing all of them in an exact pattern, each carefully briefed and ready to move. The action began about one o'clock in the afternoon, and Pancho Villa watched it from hiding.

A northbound passenger train, roaring through a mountain pass, suddenly began losing speed. Ahead of the six passenger cars were twenty-four loaded freight cars, and there was a loud rattle of couplings and brakes, spurts of smoke and dust. Because there on the track was a pileup of rocks, logs, old crossties, even the carcass of a horse. The train skidded to a stop not ten feet from it. A steam valve popped "PS-S-S-S-s-s-s-s-s!" as if by pre-arranged signal, for instantly a row of men stood up from concealment on both sides of the right-of-way. Pancho Villa, watching intently, smiled big. *"Bueno, bueno!"* he murmured. All his men carried rifles and filled cartridge belts slanted across their breasts. He felt proud of them.

Two on each side sprang to the engine cab. Others went directly to boxcar doors and began hammering them open. *Bueno,* it was according to plan. Farther down hill, the passenger cars began showing heads at windows, and finally some man there recognized the truth, Pancho observed.

"Bandidos!" that man shouted. "It is Villa's band!"

Whereupon, probably for the first time in history, came the involuntary cry that was to *make* history, the cry of adulation and loyalty that was destined to send chills up and down the spine of Mexico for years. Pancho was startled to hear it—

"VIVA VILLA!"

It broke out on the right side of the train, nearest him, then spread to both lines of attackers; dark, unshaven men, with teeth flashing in wide, happy grins, wild yet disciplined men bent on a mission of revenge against oppression. Pancho stood up, enthralled. *Viva Villa!* It was a battle cry, a victory cry. He couldn't know it then, but it was to flash from mountain to mountain, village to village, town to town, until it echoed in the very homes and cathedrals, indeed until it sent terror striding through Mexico City's presidential halls. At the moment Pancho felt an almost adolescent excitement, as if a school team had made a score. He stood there, mouth open, eyes wide, a huge young man silhouetted against the Mexican sky, astonished, unaware that he was a new symbol on the horizon.

Some humble peon turned Villista had known about axle grease spread on rails. It would stop a train going up hill, without wreckage, though the blockade of rocks and logs was an added measure. Pancho had not wanted a pileup of cars, with explosions and fires. Now in a matter of seconds his men were on and in every car. Up front the engine crew was subdued with no difficulty. After the line of freights was an express car. An armed messenger there carelessly opened a side door to peer out with his gun in hand.

"Crack!"

From outside a rifle spoke. The messenger toppled, his head striking the rock floor of the canyon.

A second worker came to the door, horrified but curious, and incautious. That too was his undoing. Villistas stepped on the two bodies to spring up into the cars and begin their looting. Leading them was a broad-shouldered, calm but very fast and powerful young man who seemed to exude efficiency in every move he made. One follower, who had known little or none of life's luxuries, saw a crate of oranges and kicked it open in order to eat. Villa slapped him.

"Stop that! You can stuff your gut later and wash it with wine. Take *that* box." He pointed to one that was iron-bound. In due time it was found to contain some $60,000 in American gold.

Other selections were made. Unlabeled crates were broken open with axes. Keys from the expressmen's bodies opened a small safe and several hundred pesos were taken, then an envelope was found to have several thousand more. Villa appraised each piece of loot with quick care and decision.

70

Meanwhile his men in the passenger and freight cars were attending to their assigned duties. From the freights came the main loot that had promoted this raid—ammunition and guns. The bandits had so many hundreds of cases that half a day was required to get them tied on pack animals for carrying away.

In the passenger section, the Villistas had their most fun. While two or three stood guard in each car, every *magnifico*, every male passenger who appeared to have any worldly goods at all, was ordered to strip naked. This he promptly did—gun muzzles can be very persuasive. At the same time Villa's men shucked off their own ragged, dingy, dirty homespun garments and dressed themselves in the stolen attire. Suitcases were opened for further items. Even watches, rings, hats, and handkerchiefs were appropriated. Many of the bandits acquired shoes, the first they had worn in years, though almost without exception they neglected to put on sox; Villa himself ordered the sox carried away to be donned later. During this interesting procedure the women passengers were permitted to hide their faces, but few did so and most just stared. It is from these that the story of train robbery has itself gained many faces; seemingly without exception each of these ladies has reported that Villa personally undressed before her and put on stolen clothes. He did no such thing, of course. He already had splendid charro costumes and a military uniform or two, even some formal evening wear, taken from ranches where he had made raids or purchased during his incognito visits to towns. His raid on the train passengers was solely to outfit his needful men.

When the bandits finally left the scene of the robbery, they could not take all their loot because they lacked enough pack animals. Only two men had been slain, both of "necessity." Enough ammunition to last indefinitely had been acquired, besides many more rifles, pistols, and officers' swords. This shipment had been ordered for a military garrison in the north, and Villa had learned of it through his new underground.

Pancho held little fear of pursuit; he ordered his loot-laden cavalcade to move away but not to rush. They would not go directly to any secret lair—he had four hideouts by this time, each stocked with food and ammunition plus whatever blankets and

71

other luxuries he had been able to get—but would divide, scatter the loot, and themselves reassemble.

"There are a hundred of us," said he to a lieutenant. "What police can bother us? In each town are two, maybe ten Rurales, eh? What can they do? Deputize a posse? But we are friends of the very ones they would have to deputize. No, only the military could pursue us, and that would take a long order from Mexico City, followed by much preparation and army doings. By then we shall be far away and safe."

It was so. There was simply no capable force to send after the new bandit prince, Pancho Villa. Much time was to pass before any effective restraint on him could be organized, and he knew it.

Ten days or so after the train robbery, Pancho ordered his men to disperse for a week then meet him again in a specified mountain valley. To each one he gave considerable riches.

"You are to take this home," he commanded. "Leave it with your families, your friends. You are not to tell where you got it except to say 'Pancho Villa gave it to me.' You understand? And it would be unwise for any one of you to mention that he rides with Villa, or to hint where Villa might be found."

When he said that last, his lips abruptly clamped tight and he glared hard into the eyes of his men for a long moment. He was giving each one time to envision what could happen to traitors. Then quietly, because these were simple men, he made the picture clear.

"One ill-begotten son of a dog spoke of getting a reward from the Rurales," said he, still glaring at them. "First, his penis was removed—chop!" He made a cutting motion with his open hand. "Then his ears—chop-chop—and his nose—" Pancho turned and beckoned. "Solano!" A man stepped forward. "Your knife." Solano unsheathed a vicious looking machete thing; Pancho took it, then finished his warning. Actually, he was lying; he had chopped no man. But he knew he had to be dramatic, had to make a good show of horror. And he rather enjoyed doing it.

Later in his own camp he explained to an aide that the men all needed their leave. Could not they, he asked, profit from a few hours to sleep with their wives, or with the girls of their choice? He himself, now—

Pancho stood up, there beside a camp table. He inhaled deeply, staring off. He snapped his lips tight—a mannerism he was unconsciously developing—and his mind reverted back to girls he too had known. Ah! His eyebrows lifted. He turned knowingly to his friends.

That week he took three of his closest henchmen to a small town and attended its Saturday plaza promenade. In this very old and charming custom (still observed in many Mexican towns) all the citizens gather in the plaza or square to listen to their band and watch the young people. Pancho and his men came onto this town's promenade unrecognized. They stood quietly watching it, smiling. Men were walking clockwise around the plaza in step with the music, girls were walking counterclockwise. When a man came abreast of the girl he preferred, he'd take her arm and dance, or escort her away for refreshment, for courting on a park bench, or for other pursuits.

"We see what we like, eh *amigos?*" Pancho murmured soon, smiling.

He moved directly across the line of marching men without joining it and boldly plucked out a beautiful girl. Some local swain might have challenged this. None did. Pancho, feeling high confidence, knew that his powerful build, his muscles plus the pistols at his side, discouraged any such thoughts.

She was pink and tan, mature but young. "I do not know you," said she, simply, huge brown eyes turned up to Pancho's.

"It is not needed that you know me. It is needed only that you have the same feeling inside you that I have inside me. *¿No es verdad, señorita?*"

She seemed to consider that, studying him, a hint of smile touching first her eyes then her lips. He sensed her growing eagerness, felt his own heart action stepping up.

"We go somewhere now, eh?" He took her arm and they walked off.

Their meeting was for less than an hour; she had a husband, she told him. But the time was enough. He did not mention his name. He learned that her husband was a peon laborer, so he gave her two pieces of gold, a fortune to her. "Have the baby," he advised. "Let him think it is his, eh? But you will remember—

73

here?" He touched her heart. "You will not forget?" It was a whispering, a tender moment.

"I will not forget," she whispered back, breathless with the sheer romance of it. "I will never forget, no matter who you are." Then she was gone.

He stood there alone for nearly half an hour longer, satisfied in body now, but still whirling in his brain. He felt good, then he felt bad; relaxed, yet unhappy. His mind calmed, then struck backward. "You must get married, Teo," his beloved Madrecita had told him. "You will hunger, and only a wife can feed what you will want, what you have already wanted. It is not something to be taken, or to be bought in a store."

He clamped his lips, forcing the thought out; slapped his huge chest and strode forward. He was no sniveling boy, eh? He was a man with a man's work to do. He took longer steps, head high. He was in his twenties now and he knew he appeared even older, more mature. A mirror, or a smooth pool of water, proved that he was not the swarthy Indian color of so many peons, but was white skinned, with a head of brown, wavy hair which always fell to the side of his forehead. Eyes were brown, and held a piercing quality. In short, the kind of man girls liked. Though still a bit disturbed by memories, he clutched at that thought and held it, taking personal inventory with satisfaction, as he made his way back to find his friends. Marriage? Why be hampered by a wife when he had riding and raiding and crusading to do? It all seemed logical to Pancho Villa.

[For the record, let it be said in passing that soon after this episode Pancho did marry; his first official wife, and one destined to outlive the several others who were to follow. She was moderately pretty; a girl named Luz Corral. His love for her did not endure, though she denied this forever. Even when he frequently returned to her, between other "wives," it was not for love, said he. At this writing Luz is old and fat, embittered and poverty-haunted, yet reasonably gracious and kind.]

8

P<small>ANCHO</small> soon lost count of the raids that he made on the ranches of the rich.

"We have much success, eh?" said he to a captain in his ranks, Pascual Herrera, one Sunday morning. "You go now to mass, Pascual. You say the thanks for us."

"Say your own thanks, big man," Pascual countered. "I have trouble enough getting myself into heaven."

"Heaven! Me, I never get there."

"Likely you won't, you big bastard."

Pancho had been preening himself before a mirror. Now he turned on his friend in mock anger. "Who you call that?"

For a long moment they wrestled, straining, panting, cursing one another, acting like the young roosters they were. It was a rare moment for Pancho, really; a leader can seldom enjoy such companionship.

"You capture too many ranches to get into heaven," Pascual ruled, sitting back in his chair. "Besides, the angels wouldn't have you. You always stink of sweat and garlic."

"*Me?*"

They discussed this vital detail. A leader, a bandit chieftain, must be a Personality, *no es verdad?* He must be refined. Well then, he would bathe oftener. He would give up garlic forever— an oath that he kept for almost a week.

He felt himself to be in the prime of masculine perfection. So he bore himself proudly. His perfect gleaming teeth seemed to light up his life when he smiled, which was often; and he knew that the vibrant energy of him was contagious. Conceit? The thought entered his mind, right enough, and he meditated on it.

"Is not conceit," he told himself, actually murmuring it, one day while dressing in his charro costume. "It is not conceit to know what one has. Is it conceit to know one has pistols? A dagger? A rifle? Money? Well then. It is not conceit to know one has, ah, looks, eh?"

"Oyez, Pancho! You called me?"

That was Pascual again, from the next room. Pancho blushed;

he had begun speaking louder without realizing it. Now he reacted quickly, covering up.

"I was saying a man must have confidence, Pascual. I congratulate you, my friend. You are sure of yourself, you do not whine to me to decide everything you do."

Pascual came in, slightly embarrassed. "Thank you," he managed. But he was slightly puzzled too.

"Confidence is not conceit, Pascual."

"¿Que dice?"

"Shut the mouth, friend. I was talking to myself." The lips clamped. Pascual, an astute lieutenant, said no more.

The Villa self-awareness became more and more valuable, as Villa himself well realized. It enabled him to achieve many more successes in the ensuing weeks. After four months of intense activity, he sat once more for a few days of relaxation in a distant hidden camp, and there he took inventory again. This time, of group efforts made.

"Four more ranches, six stagecoaches, six trains and eight train stations, some mine offices, stores," he was ticking them off on his fingers. "And we have given money and clothing and food to—how many poor people, Pascual?"

Pascual could only guess. Maybe two thousand, said he. It was gratifying to both men; robbing the arrogant rich to pay the poor for years of bondage.

The time came when Pancho felt that he must dethrone the greatest cattle baron of all. "Pascual," said he one day, "when I was hiding in the mountains I made jerky of some steers branded like this." He squatted to sketch in the sand:

Pascual spat, in contempt.

"Ah ha, you know it, eh?"

"Terrazas."

"Si, amigo. Don Luis. His is the biggest ranch in the world, people say. It has five big haciendas."

"You would capture the Don Luis Terrazas rancho, Pancho? Man, it is an empire!"

"Sit down. We make some plans."

It was truly an empire, 6,000,000 acres and 300,000 head of cattle. Pancho's peons could not envision the grandeur of it. Don Luis himself lived like a grandee in old Spain. The richest men and women of Mexico adorned his five homes; the nation's foremost painters, sculptors, authors, and musicians favored him with their presence. In his patios were held the world's most lavish fiestas, often lasting for weeks. He owned fabulously rich mines, factories, towns, churches, railroads, herds of horses, everything. Whence came such opulence? Ask Pancho Villa. Ask *any* man reared as a peon to bare his back. There in scars would be the answer.

Pancho felt certain that Don Luis had heard of him by now. He knew that newspapers and word-of-mouth stories about him had spread his fame. But he was equally certain that Don Luis paid little attention to any Villa talk. The Terrazas ranch was self sufficient, Pascual warned Pancho. Most of its riders were armed. Many bandits, so called, had popped up in Chihuahua over the years, stolen from some of the ranch stores, then been ridden down and killed. One more could do nothing beyond annoy some of the don's isolated villages or towns. If one ever got so bold as to stop a Terrazas train, then of course he would have to be eliminated *pronto*. True, Villa was said to have quite a following, maybe two hundred or more men, thus making him the most important bandit in recent years. But what of that? If he had two thousand, what of it? Don Luis Terrazas needed only to telegraph Mexico City and any required number of cavalrymen would be sent at once to ride the bandit to his doom. Such was the feeling on the great rancho, Pascual told his friend.

Pancho listened, grinned big, and announced his plan. Wherefore, one rosy dawn the watchmen and then night workers at the biggest Terrazas hacienda were startled out of their sleepy lethargy by an explosion of human voices matched in history only by the American rebel yell.

"EE-YAH-YAH-YAH-YAH-YEOW!"

It was shrill and penetrating; it came from hundreds of men in blood-chilling crescendo, and the thunderous background for it was a staccato of horses' hoofs. It was like the attack of Apache Indians, for the riders circled the ranch home as if wrapping a noose around it for strangulation, which indeed they were. Its circumference grew rapidly smaller, and each leap of a man's horse seemed punctuated by the sharp bark of a gun. The marksmen were unbelievably accurate. In their hidden mountain valleys

77

Pancho Villa had trained them for just this kind of fighting, had made them run, learning to guide their horses by knee pressures alone, and to shoot, re-load and shoot again at small targets. Thus in a matter of seconds the windows of the hacienda were black, sightless eyes in the sunrise glow. Any defender who dared show himself was, of course, promptly dispatched to eternally green pastures. "VIVA VILLA!" shrieked the mad men, as six dismounted to batter down the big double front doors. Don Luis? He was not present. Good fortune had enabled him to be away on business. Only token resistence was offered the Villistas.

Within the hour the bandits had collected such loot as they had never encountered before. Only a few men had been assigned to this work. They were well disciplined; they could be trusted to gather loot for all, Pancho knew, carefully watching.

Pancho himself stayed outside. Because, as he would have entered the beautiful home with his men, he heard a cry from a group of peons not his own, the magic "VIVA VI-I-I-I-LA!"

Quickly he remounted and galloped down there, feeling high indeed. It was at the workers' village. The men and women and children, hundreds strong, once more had poured out in hysterical welcome, he observed. Women shouted "Viva Villa!" over and over, waving old towels, their black shawls or *rebozos*, their kitchen rags, any sort of banners they could contrive. He saw the new hope that he had brought them.

When he galloped close he reined up so suddenly that his big black stallion skidded then reared, its proud head high, its bridle and saddle ornaments rattling. Ah, what a picture Pancho made —and he himself well knew it! He waved to the peons, shrieking in happy hysteria. He waved back then shouted "Thank you from my heart!"

He swung down, and instantly was surrounded. It is good, he told himself, beaming, that I am tall. They all but crushed him and he loved it. Women were crying, laughing, shrieking, holding out babies for him to touch. Men pushed close, holding out hands, straining to get to Pancho in the flesh. He tried to stay calm, tried to count the people as their number grew. He decided there were more than a thousand.

Escape from them was not easy, but when two smiling and happy lieutenants "rescued" him he waved farewell and dashed dramatically off. A few minutes later, a mile away, he dismounted again, walked off to one side and in the presence of his two companions, began to unbutton his trousers.

"Be damn!" swore he, who rarely swore. "They make me so

excited I damn near wet my britches. What is the reason for that?"

Wetting copiously, he saw his men only spread their hands and shrug in reply. They had no answer, nor did he. His lips firmed in a moment of anger, at his kidneys. It had happened before when he was excited. He remembered—here with victory high in his mind—that he had used to wet the shuck mattress in his mother's home, and it had always embarrassed him. Now some instinct told him that the problem would live with him to the end of his days, especially in moments of excitement. He cursed again.

When he got back to the hacienda the looting was nearly complete, and his men were wild with victory. He saw that Don Luis Terrazas' hand-picked retinue of defenders had disappeared, and that the main houses were now over-run with peons stripping whatever the Villistas had left. Pancho, avoiding more demonstrations, sent orders to depart, and within half an hour his band were riding two abreast, a long serpentine of men drunken with power, winding through the Chihuahuan hills.

He knew there were other Terrazas haciendas, so methodically he attacked them in the days that followed. Without problems, they fell to his hands. "Nobody shoots much at us," he told a reporter who had located him, a man from the United States. "We go in, free the workers, take what we need, and go on about our business." He wondered if the American, the *gringo*, could understand his attitude here; could understand what it meant to be free of peonage.

Successes on the big ranch raids caused Pancho next to consider attacking the border city of Juarez. He knew it was important, for several reasons. It had influence, it was big, it would mean high prestige for the Villistas if they could successfully raid it. And—it truly could supply money, clothing, and food for the peons whose cause he espoused. Thus he reasoned to his close henchmen. They agreed with him after long consideration. Juarez had size, hence great potential. It had many stores with much valuable merchandise. It also had a rather strong military garrison.

But the time was not yet. Villa, learning fast, soon realized what many another conqueror has not—that you must consolidate what you conquer. This was explained to him by one of the now several educated men who had joined his band.

"There is no value just in the taking of vast areas of land, Pancho," this one said. "Even Genghis Khan lost the world by conquering too much of it too fast."

"Who is he?" Pancho the peon glowered. He turned to face his friend, sensing a new opponent in the upstart Khan.

He saw the friend laugh, then himself smiled, waiting, alert. "Señor Khan raided centuries ago on another continent. Forget it."

Pancho forgot nothing, ever; he filed a tiny mental note about this Khan. Later, in a campfire hour, he made his friend tell all he knew about that earlier conqueror.

Today, though, Pancho reiterated to his friend that " I do not wish to rule, *amigo*. I want to liberate."

He saw the friend nod agreement. "Right, right. You steal only to help the poor. A Robin Hood—I have told you already about that Englishman, eh?"

Now Pancho nodded. Hood's story had appealed greatly to him.

"Even so, Pancho, what you have now is no longer just a picturesque band of adventurers, out for some romantic didoes of rascality and fun. You have a strong army. Understand?"

"Army?" Pancho stared at him, brows, knitted.

"Exactly. And history has shown few if any strong armies that did not almost immediately find abundant fighting to do."

Pancho continued staring, bewildered now for sure. Never in his life had he dreamed of leading a Mexican army. Dreamed of being a soldier—yes; that's different. But for a barefoot peon to think of rising high, of actually commanding—no. A bolt of lightning could strike you for such presumption.

He swallowed hard; cupped chin in his hand, thinking. He looked down, then back at his friend. "What do you mean?" he finally demanded.

The friend was succinct. "You heard me. You're no fool. I mean you have jockeyed yourself high up the ladder."

Pancho glowered fiercely at him. "An *army?*"

The friend nodded. "An army. Ragtag, maybe, but an army no less. And a reputation to go with it. A reputation for conquest."

"I be damn." He was speaking the limited English he had learned. But he was speaking more to himself, in astonishment; trying to clarify things.

"Armies are run by governments, Pancho. So—" the friend shrugged expressively. "You are getting close to governmental toes. *¿Sabe usted?*

Handsome Pancho slowly shook his head, bewilderment still showing. "No. No no, *amigo*. Me, I not government. Not army."

He made negative motions with his hand.

"The hell you aren't! Any time you've got two or three thousand men under arms, and as many more trying to join you, you've got an army. And as for government—well, hell, you know who Porfirio Diaz is."

"*El presidente, si.*" Pancho had heard of the president; he lived and presumably worked—at something or other—away off to the south in the City of Mexico; much too far away to have any bearing on Pancho's personal life.

"Well, pal, it's Diaz who has caused all the oppression of the poor peons whom you are trying to help." Thus said the friend.

Pancho was frowning, straining to understand; conscious now of his own ignorance, and angered by it. The lecture continued. He decided that if Diaz had caused the peons' bondage, then the Villistas were against Diaz.

In due time a rebel arose to combat Diaz, and his name was Madero. So, Pancho now was for Madero. He began to ask many questions about Madero, mostly of American newsmen. He learned that Madero had run for president; that Diaz had driven him out of the country on a trumped-up charge; that Madero had then come back to Mexico to lead a rebellion against the "re-elected" Diaz. That made up Pancho's mind for sure. He was not immediately concerned, of course, but if ever opportunity presented itself, Pancho told his henchmen, he'd certainly throw his weight on Madero's side.

He tried to dismiss the matter from his mind. With several hundred men to train in horsemanship, shooting, fighting, he had plenty to do. He had an instinct for excellence in working with his men, so he drove them, drove his appointed lieutenants and sergeants, who in turn demanded the best skills the Villa followers could produce.

Then one night an American newspaperman said to him, "Pancho, what you need is a course of study. You need to know politics."

"Who he?" Pancho demanded.

The *gringo* barely smiled. "It's not a he. Not one man, Pancho. It's—well, several men. It's the government. The things that go on in the government. Pancho, have you ever been to school?"

"*No señor.*"

"Mm-m-m-m, well." The newsman sounded ominous. "There's a lot you need to know, my friend."

"What? What I need to know?"

"Everything, man! You're not a peanut performer any more.

81

You're big time. Don't you understand?" The reporter was in earnest, and spoke in exasperation. Pancho studied him, trying to grasp something from the man's English, his own being so limited. He didn't succeed.

That night at dinner he sat apart from the usual little group of henchmen that ate with him. He said nothing, but he made it plain that he wanted to be alone. He took a stool and plopped it near their camp fire. A cook brought him a bowl of stew.

He looked at it, frowned, threw bowl and all into the darkness. "*Carne,*" he growled.

The man hastened off, returned soon with a huge cut of beef that had been half cooked over coals, and a small loaf of bread. Pancho speared the meat with his belt knife and began to bite off it while gazing into the blaze of the campfire. He saw no one, he wanted to think. As he sat there thinking, he ate prodigiously; devoured that huge hunk of meat and that medium sized loaf of bread, then called for more. No one dared disturb him.

He knew that he was over-eating; knew that he always did so when disturbed. Other men, he had observed, took to drink on such occasions; got themselves fired up on tequila. He rarely ever touched the stuff. It seemed to clog his mind; and it affected his kidneys, or he thought it did. So he over-ate, trying to think. He wished he could go home. He wished he could go back this night to his Madrecita, she now long gone. Maybe *she* would know about—what was the *gringo* word?—pol, politics.

The whole thing worried him, and he was unaccustomed to worry, he was a man of action. Tonight, however, some sure instinct told him that fate was pushing him, and that he was ill prepared.

9

HE WAS standing on a boulder thirty feet or so high one afternoon, bareheaded, and motionless as if he had been carved from the stone itself. Indeed he looked like a part of it; rock hard, tan-brown of costume and skin hue. He would have made an excellent target for any rifleman even at long range, and he knew it; but this was his own lair, this was his camp. From the boulder he could look down on the columns of horsemen being trained in a pasture-like valley. He had already briefed his lieutenants.

"Nobody is ever good enough on a horse," he spoke with vigor, issuing his orders. "Pick out the cocky ones, the fellows who say they are experts. Give them the wildest horses, set them the fastest runs and turns, and make them shoot at beer bottles while leaning low."

"But Pancho," one lieutenant dared protest, "some already are perfect, and have their own horses. They will not want to change."

With that, he roared in quick anger, adding logically "And if their favorite horses are shot from under them? If they then have to grab the first horse in sight, a strange one? Hah!"

That ended the discussion; the training was under way. He stood now to windward, so that spurts of hoof dust went down slope in waves that darkened the shrubbery for half a mile. Hoofs made a constant rumble as of thunder, broken by the staccato *crack, crack-crack* of rifle fire. With gratification he saw beer bottles explode, glass pinpointing the sun rays back at him as bullets struck. A man with his chest on his saddle horn shooting from a horse whose ears were laid back and legs were extended in full speed ahead, could be proud if he hit a beer bottle at thirty, twenty, even ten yards. Some hits were made at fifty, he noted, white teeth gleaming in a smile. If the target had been a man, hits doubtless would total high at 100 yards. He himself had worked long at this, and often practiced. Besides being good insurance, it was a good sport, it was calming to the nerves.

"It takes the fire out of a man's groins," he had philosophized once, to a friend. "Ride hard in a saddle for four hours, lean, shoot, swing about, twist and turn. That night you sleep, you do not lie awake wanting a woman." He spoke from experience.

His lieutenants had switched the men to mounting exercises when he reached for his hat to put it back on. He'd have to show them a thing or two. You leaped from hiding—any hiding—ran fast and *jumped* to your horse's back. The horse must be galloping fast in the next instant. You must control everything with knee pressures; your hands would be too busy either shooting the rifle or swinging it as a club. Or maybe you'd be swinging a sword if you had one. A few men did have. You rode with your legs, you fought with your arms and hands. He was proud of that skill.

But as he turned to go he saw five horsemen approaching from a trail to his side. He knew four were sentinels. They had been posted down trail two miles or more. Obviously they had a

83

captive now, for he carried no arms. Pancho waited, wondering.

He waited in silence until they halted near his rock and looked up at him. He sensed his advantage; any man, above another, is tacitly in command. He didn't have to ask his own men what they wanted.

"You look for something, *señor?*" Pancho inquired, with full courtesy.

The captive, no peon but obviously a man of good rank, and unafraid, impressed Pancho with his demeanor, his bearing, even the way he sat his horse.

"I look for Pancho Villa," said the man.

"Well now!" Pancho's white teeth gleamed. "Many people look for him. The Rurales. The military. The ranchers and their contemptible hirelings. And now you. It is hoped that you have bid your loved ones farewell?"

"I am not afraid, *señor*. I am a friend of Pancho Villa though I have never met him. He will not kill a man who comes openly this way to see him, bearing a message."

Pancho liked that. The two eyed each other in a moment of silence. Curiosity touched Pancho.

"What message?"

"I come not for myself, but as a message bearer from Francisco I. Madero. I bring his greetings and good wishes to Colonel Francisco Villa."

"*Colonel* Villa?" Pancho laughed. "Do you know who I am?" The stranger nodded, serious faced.

"Hah! I am no colonel. I am no army man at all. I am Pancho."

"I think of the future, sir. I am instructed by His Excellency to say that Mexico calls."

Pancho's brows furrowed as he studied the man, trying to comprehend. He was in no mood to kill him; anyway instinct told him of sincerity. Abruptly he slid down from his rock and beckoned with a toss of his head.

Walking the two hundred yards or so to his headquarters tent, with the five riders a respectful distance behind him, he tried to think this out. *Colonel* Villa. What did that mean? What did a colonel do that he wasn't already doing? A title, yes; it sounded fine, and maybe it commanded respect, eh? He didn't need one, to command respect. His magic pistols commanded respect, they and his hearty grin, his friendliness, his reputation. So why a colonel?

The messenger explained at length. It was an oddly formal conference, for Pancho. He wasn't used to this sort of thing, and had

84

to feel his way. The man used excellent Spanish; used words Pancho had never heard before, although he could piece together the man's meanings, and grasp the news he brought.

Madero, he learned, was but thirty-three years of age, hence only a few months different from Pancho. He had proclaimed himself a Redeemer, the messenger said.

"What's that?" Pancho demanded.

The man explained. Madero wanted to help poor people, even as Villa did. Madero appealed to emotions of people in Chihuahua and in Texas as well, the Texans because they had been unhappy over border relations with Diaz. Pancho, pleased, nodded his approval.

Madero also had raised a ragtag army in a hurry, Pancho learned. For quick prestige he had moved on such small towns as Cerro Prieta, Mal Paso, Guerro, Janos. They had negligible garrisons, so Madero captured them with a flourish. Pancho smiled big at this. He understood the technique and approved it, for it matched his own. Like Pancho Villa then, Madero had stature in the peons' eyes, he too was making a dream come true. Pancho felt a kinship.

In the end, Pancho accepted his title of Colonel. It never occured to him to wonder if it was "official;" if Madero had any authority to confer such a title, or if it had any real meaning. Colonel! The sound of it was flattering.

"I have been made a colonel," he informed his hitherto rather rough and informal aides, his lieutenants-in-fact, his co-adventurers.

The statement implied much. From it they inferred correctly, Pancho noted. He now had rank; from some source whose very distance and vagueness seemed to give it Authority. Pancho, shrewd enough to sense all this, decided it was wise to let it grow. One of his closest aides was shrewd in turn, he noted; this one immediately taught everybody around to salute, and hinted that it was wise to do so. Pancho overheard much of this, observed more of it, and grinned.

"Be damn," he said to an American news hawk some days later. "Me, Pancho Villa, I just friend, just pal, eh, who shoot good, slap backs, goose girls in behinds, make laughs, give money to poor peoples. But *Colonel* Villa—hah! This is different."

The difference astonished even him. He wasn't sure how to conduct himself in his new colonelcy. Lacking military training, he felt ill at ease. "What I do?" he demanded of the newsman. "How a man colonel, eh?"

"'Colonel' is not a verb, Pancho—oh hell, you wouldn't know a verb from a subjunctive nominative predicate—look, friend, you just act important. ¿Sabe usted? A colonel doesn't buddy-buddy around with—with privates and such. He *is* important, so you act like it. Be a leader."

Pancho grasped that, and by intuition followed the counsel. In private he practiced returning salutes. He decided to be snappy with it— a quick turn of the hat brim—staring straight ahead. He liked that. He had seen many officials salute one another. It had never occurred to him that he'd receive or do any saluting, but—

"You have risen to new place," he informed himself, practicing there in his tent, adjusting his uniform jacket, resetting his hat. He was very self-conscious with it all but he was enjoying it too. A mental flashback of the boy Doroteo Arango invaded him for a long moment. Doroteo would have loved this! Doroteo the peon lad who wrangled horses back yonder years ago. Now receiving respectful salutes.

Pancho felt young again. And a bit wistful.

His colonelcy, it developed, was no play title, no comic opera thing. This surprised him a little, but he grew with events. Before he quite realized it, he had been trusted with Madero's most secret plans.

They were good plans; good, because they were idealistic, and Pancho heartily approved of them. Madero had been a blessing unexpected; an ally out of the blue. Pancho's—no, Colonel Villa's —small "army" was in good spirits; hard, well trained, anxious to go. Pancho felt that they were a very strong military force. Weren't they commanded now by a colonel, no less?

He assumed there could be no trouble; a genuine official "general" such as Madero would have detail in hand, eh? He didn't reason further than that, didn't inquire even of himself as to just who had made Madero a general. The title was impressive enough.

Nevertheless, Colonel Pancho Villa was careful, and eager to learn. The American newsmen, as always, were his best teachers. In the lull of preparations here he revealed his military secrets to only a select few, among them a distant cousin named Claro Reza. Reza had sworn absolute loyalty, and Pancho, knowing him as a man of education, had been impressed, had felt that Reza was needed, could be valuable. Then one day an older friend came to Colonel Villa.

"You do not know your cousin, Claro Reza, very well? You do not know that he is a son-in-law of Don Luis Terrazas?"

Pancho jumped from his chair. "No!"

The informant shrugged. "Yes. Another thing you do not know —he is a friend of Enrique S. Creel, the Governor of Chihuahua. He is in Creel's secret service."

Pancho broke into cursing, grabbed the man, and shook his shoulders. "Then he will tell everything he knows of the revolution! He will reveal all of Madero's plans!"

"Of a certainty, Colonel Villa. It is why I come. You wish proof? I have papers here."

There remained, then, only one thing to do. Pancho wanted to do it personally instead of delegating it. He knew where Reza was to be found. Reza had gone to a town to do a little spying for Villa himself, checking its strength and its possible military advantage if taken. It was not a stronghold, but it might be. Risking his own capture, disdaining any sort of bodyguard, the impulsive bandit leader got his finest horse and rode alone to the town.

At a distance he saw Reza in front of a grocery store, unmounted. He felt no qualms, made no hesitation. His eyes narrowed and he spurred his horse, then reined up with a flourish of stampings and dust and was on the ground in an instant.

"Reza, you squealing dog!" he cried.

He would have talked with the man, would have made the treason clear, but in that instant Reza went for his guns. They did him no good. Pancho's actions were involuntary, from long training; the now famous twin .45's leaped from their holsters as if on springs and roared in unison. He stood there taut, poised like a reptile ready for a second strike, nerveless, dangerous. He watched as Reza's body went slack then crumpled into the dirt and filth that always adorned the front of a village store in Mexico. He felt no pangs of conscience. A traitor had been discovered, a traitor had deserved to die; killing him brought the satisfaction of justice done. Still eyeing the body, he automatically reloaded his pistol chambers, slowly, deliberately.

Men came running, then slowed and stopped, watching in awe. He gave them no greeting, though he saw that he was recognized. A mangy mongrel dog heard the excitement and trotted up, sniffed the body once, looked around in confusion, then bayed. It was Reza's requiem. Pancho half smiled. He knew that nobody would touch the body for hours, maybe days. Because removing it might tag you as Reza's friend, and it was better if people assumed you to be Pancho Villa's friend instead. For this reason he lingered ten minutes or so, grim faced, erect in his saddle, watching, lifting a hand now and then as other men appeared. The body was like a magnet, the killer like a cocked gun. So he heard the men speak only in low tones, showing respect. He wanted to be seen, wanted the message to be thoroughly absorbed. When he was satisfied, he kneed his horse and dashed away in a roll of dust.

Riding alone back to his headquarters, Colonel Villa did a lot of earnest thinking. He had slowed the fine horse to its restful rocking hunk-of-meat-and-chili-pepper rhythm, a "singlefoot" that covered ground and tired neither man nor beast. Reza's treachery had impressed him. There might be other Rezas; he'd have to do a quiet study, a weeding out process. As colonel he had obligations, he couldn't just roll along in haphazard bandit fashion any more, he told himself rather grandly.

He gave further thought also to his ignorance. This had disturbed him more and more of late, but there had been a crumb of comfort, he recalled. "Recognition of ignorance is the beginning of wisdom," an American newspaper reporter had quoted, explaining it in detail. At least he knew he had much to learn. So, sitting his horse easily, riding alone, Colonel Doroteo Arango Francisco Villa wondered if it were feasible for him *now* to attend school. The thought intrigued him. He had never been to any school; the problem in his youth had been staying alive, not educating oneself. And so life had cheated him. But if he, in his thirties, went to school now—

He grinned at his little-boy yearning, yet not without sadness, not without wistful wishing. The killing of Claro Reza? It had been dismissed from his mind, a necessary chore completed. Once as a boy in his mother's home he had been called on to kill a dog dying of sores, and he had done it, grimly, without pleasure but without worry too. It was like that with the men killed in battle, more so with Reza. So, now his mind was solely on his mind's limitations. Instinct told him this was to haunt him all his life, this lack.

He filled his immediate needs in some measure by talking with ex-soldiers, news men and others who knew something of army life. Thus a week after his return to camp, he observed with gratification that his erstwhile peon bandits were doing squads left, squads right, platoon left, platoon right, on the drill field, and in reasonably good order. A few protested that they were riders, not walkers; these Colonel Villa put through an hour of double-time trotting, then asked them if they wished to leave his army. None did; none dared, and he knew they wouldn't. One hot day nineteen men fainted, so harsh was his training. One died apparently of heart attack. Though their tongues grew cottony with thirst and fatigue, most of the men found the drill exhilarating, Pancho observed; and he made a special point of complimenting them. Their reward was to be moved to horseback again. Well drilled now on foot, they understood the maneuvering in cavalry formations too.

After sixty days of it, Colonel Francisco Villa had soldiers who could stand at rigid attention for hours if need be, or who could rush to their horses, saddle, mount, and be ready to charge before the average man could shuck off his pajamas. The colonel enjoyed timing them, pitting teams against teams. The horses seemed to love cavalry life too, though it must have been taxing on them. The colonel was strict about caring for the animals. When a young rider forgot to feed his mount one night, Pancho made the rider himself go without food for twenty-four hours. Their horses learned the commands, learned the bugle calls. They even seemed to recognize their commander when he himself leaned low and raced to their lead, shouting and waving his sword. In all of this, Doroteo Arango lived again, Doroteo the boy wrangler. Alone in his tent he admitted to himself that he had never been happier; the two months training had been fun, as playing at warfare has always been.

It ceased to be play rather abruptly. Pancho's scouts had been out, and reporting regularly. One night he issued quiet orders. Next morning he led five hundred picked men racing up the dry bed of the Rio Chuviscar. They swung over its steep banks and went roaring into that capital of the northland, Chihuahua City.

"EE-YAH-YAH-YAH-YAH-H-H-H-H!" the Villistas yelled in their explosion of terror. "VIVA VI-I-I-I-I-LLA-A-A-A-A!"

He hadn't taught them that. But he liked it and sensed its worth. He was not Pancho here, he was Colonel Villa. Or—was he? The very question came to mind even as his horse plunged toward the city, and soon he knew the answer. He was nominally colonel, but he would forever be Pancho to the men, Pancho Villa. It was a dual role, somewhat unique in warfare as his instincts told him. He liked it, knew it was good.

Chihuahua City fought back.

From the fortress on the hill, cannons boomed. Most of his men had never heard a cannon before, nor indeed had he. It was red thunder. It was the roar of doom. Pancho, wide-eyed with wonder, had a premonition but he tried to ignore it. He waved his men on.

From the thick stone walls federalist rifles cracked. From windows and doorways, from behind earthen embankments, seemingly from everywhere, bullets came *splat, splat*. Pancho found that some of his riders had dashed up this street, some up that, others into alleys and courtyards. He tried to re-group them, but it was hard to find more than a dozen together, and when he did find these, more than likely half would be bleeding, a strange horror in their eyes. It was as if they looked at him with astonishment, blaming him who had led them to think they were invincible. He felt his own confidence draining like life blood itself.

He dashed around a corner and came unexpectedly onto a handsome young recruit, his bugler.

"Blow assembly!" Pancho yelled.

They had no call for retreat; hadn't practiced any, hadn't thought to need any. But they had one for assembly, and had agreed to assemble "after the victory" at a specified place. Pancho thanked God for it now.

It served well. The disorganized, even terrified Villistas heard the welcome sound, swerved their horses and raced away with bullets clipping the dust behind them. Pancho stayed near, encouraging them as best he could. Six hours later, sitting alone once more in his tent, he realized that he had been to school after all. It was a grim thought, yet he grinned at it, at himself, at his recent whimsy and yearning. School? What better one than Experience?

One thing learned was that Chihuahua City had been defended by a force three times as strong as his own. Accustomed to swift victory with a hundred or two men, he had tacitly assumed that five hundred would be invincible. What remained of them now (about three hundred and forty) were chastened men. They too had been "educated," their leader grimly told himself.

Next day he rode among his encamped men to feel out their tempers, and he was pleasantly surprised. They were defeated but not cowed. What if the first round of a fight is lost, if you personally come out unscarred? The next round may be yours!

That philosophy was inspiriting. He responded to it, learning still, from the very men under his command. He discovered that many never actually knew they had been defeated at Chihuahua

City, they had simply obeyed the bugle call, and they still trusted Pancho implicitly. This knowledge left him a little awed.

"I be gaw damn!" he exclaimed, telling about it to an American newsman who had, inevitably, turned up at his door. "I make the—how you say, *amigo?*—the mess of theengs, and they don' know him! Beeg fool, me! They think I am their papa, my mens."

"Congratulations, Colonel. Few leaders command such loyalty."

"Hah. What I do now, eh?" The powerful young leader rumpled his own hair, striding around his tent, trying to clear his thinking.

"What you do now? You get the hell out of this blue funk you are in, first thing. You've been over-eating like a damned hog." The newsman smiled; it wouldn't do to speak harshly to Pancho Villa without smiling. "You always over-eat after you've had trouble, did you know that?"

"*Si, si.*" Pancho reverted to Spanish, speaking sadly, chastened.

"Well cut it out. The hunger is not in your gut, man, it's in your mind. Feed your mind, not your belly."

"How do I do those?"

"Hell, I don't know. Will power, I guess—what else? Just don't let your men see you hang-dogging around feeling sorry for yourself."

Pancho nodded. "*Si, si.* You right. *Mil gracias.* I make you reech, I give you bag of gold, my fran', for help me."

"Keep your damned gold, or give it to some starving mother. That's your life, isn't it, Robin? Robin Hood? Taking it from the rich, giving it to the poor? For that alone, Colonel, I bother to respect you. And I guess it's enough."

It took him a while to get over the shame of that defeat in Chihuahua City. He feared a reprimand from General Madero, who had made him a colonel. None came. But within the month another supporter of Madero, one Pascual Orozco, came to his attention. Orozco had gathered a small group of fighters also, and sent a messenger saying that he would be willing to join Villa's army.

This offer gave Pancho new life. He welcomed recruits with much fanfare, even a celebration, an all-male fiesta that included such bizarre doings as a contest to see which soldier could urinate the farthest. Pancho himself suggested it, and himself won first prize—a bottle of *tequila,* the fiery drink made from juice of the

Mexican century plant. He gave it to a bearded private.

"Me, I don't drink much liquor," he explained. "It makes my head like a merry-go-round."

"I understand," said his new lieutenant, Pascual Orozco. "You are a leader, colonel, you have to think clearly."

The contest itself, he had also to explain to an enthralled American reporter who witnessed it, was nothing new. He, Pancho, had often won such contests when he was a boy horse wrangler. Boys enjoyed competing, often even with girl spectators. He had always won. Saying so gave him an odd satisfaction now.

Orozco's arrival with reinforcements brought new life to both groups. Spirits soared again. When an outrider brought Pancho word that a detachment of *Federalistas*—Diaz soldiers—was coming next morning into the State of Chihuahua on a freight train, the bandit colonel grinned gleefully and laid plans for revenge. Had not he and a few barefoot bandits taken one train a while ago, gathering much good loot? Of a surety, my compadres! Well then, we know how. We will take this one easily, gather more rifles and ammunition, food and uniforms, and a lot of Federal prisoners as well. Bravo, let us make ready!

When the train slowed from the axle grease on its rails next morning, the two lines of rebels arose on the right-of-way as before, shouting "VIVA VILLA!" and quick-firing their rifles at the train. Pancho felt high elation. But then—

"*Tat-tat-tat-tat-tat-tatt-tatt!*"

A strange new battle sound broke out under the shrieking.

"*Tat-tat-tat-tat-tat.*" Pause. *Tat-tat-tat. Tat-tat-tat-tat.*

The short bursts of it were almost hypnotic, coming from not one but from twenty or thirty box cars, with staccato spurts of flame punctuating like exclamation marks. Pancho stared, incredulous, appalled. In rhythm with the bursts, rows of big-hatted Villistas fell to the ground, like dominoes that had stood on end and been toppled. Colonel Villa couldn't believe his eyes.

His buglers all knew a call for retreat now; they had practiced it on orders. Retreat and re-group at a safe distance. In the confusion a sergeant gave command for it to be blown, which was just as well. The bugler on the other side of the track picked it up. Pancho Villa, for once, was at wit's end. The *tat-tat-tat* sound, the dropping men, had left him utterly bewildered, and furious once more at his own ignorance.

92

In a few minutes uniformed Federalist privates had run up front of the locomotive and removed the Villa blockade. Others had scooped sand onto the rails.

"WHOOOO, WHOOT- WHOO-O-O-O!" the engine shrieked, then huffed and puffed in defiance. The soldiers piled back on and their train was again under its way.

Pancho Villa, stunned, looked down at the scene of the fiasco. Rows of men lay dead or writhing in agony. He and they had been introduced to that spectacular war-winning new weapon, the machine gun.

10

For the next thirty hours or so Pancho didn't sleep, didn't eat, and paused only two or three times to swallow a mug of water. He was nursing a deep fury while he helped to gather and tend his wounded men. Only one person in his command could be called a doctor, and because of the shattering defeat he promptly got drunk. Pancho found him supine on the sand, and at first though him dead.

"Bury him," he ordered, kicking the body to make sure.

The body groaned. Pancho straddled him, lifted him by the belt, examined him, then tried to shake him back to sensibility. The doctor managed to open his eyes blearily and grin. Pancho slapped him and went on.

When the worst of the makeshift first aid was finished, he tried to take inventory of men and material remaining. Because his trusted lieutenants had been shot down, he couldn't do a good job of it. Finally he fell asleep on a saddle blanket, planning to rest just half an hour.

Twelve hours later he awoke, found himself in a tent on a cotton mattress with blankets, sheets, and pillow. Stiff and sore, he forced himself to sit up. His mind focused again, and the horror of defeat came back to him. He stroked his dirty long-unshaved face, ran fingers through tousled hair. He stank with his own dried sweat.

"Be damn," he muttered to himself, in English.

A barefoot boy stuck his head in the tent. "*Señor* Colonel?"

He didn't answer; didn't feel like talking. The boy disappeared and presently came back with hot breakfast, sat it near Pancho, and disappeared again. Pancho sat barelegged on the edge of his camp cot and ate. He felt starved. He also felt irreparably depressed. He was plainly a failure, he would now be a fugitive for all time. His life was done.

He was so uncomfortable that he left his cot and walked outside half naked to find a toilet spot. From there he saw a stream. He remembered he had picked this as a good campsite; water is imperative. Ten or twelve women were there now, washing clothes. He knew them to be women of his lieutenants and junior officers who were permitted to have wives or mistresses along. He ignored them, plodded on down to the stream within a few yards of them, shucked off his undershorts. The moment the women discovered him their motions and their talking ceased.

It was as if they didn't exist. Colonel Villa, stark naked, waded into the water like a thirsty ox, submerged, came up blowing and slapping his body, shaking his great head with coal-colored hair thick over the ears. The water chilled him, sent his blood racing, and this he knew was good. He gave vent to his feelings once—"Whow-w-w-w-w-w-www!"—a long, luxurious exhalation as he floated face up looking only at the sky. Ten minutes later he splashed ashore, slinging water off his torso with bare hands, and walked back to his tent. The servant boy had anticipated his need and met him with fresh dry clothing. Nobody had spoken; nobody spoke now. He was grateful for the silence.

The food and the bath restored him, and he came out forcing a smile. But it was a poor "army" that he faced. He took quick mental inventory again, dismissed all the wounded who could walk, and regrouped those soldiers who were unharmed. There were more than he had thought. His spirits had been revived by rest and food anyway, and the apparent loyalty of his remaining men further heartened him. All that day he directed new formations, new drills. He realized that his men sensed a new attitude in him. Defeat had changed him. But it had not killed his determination.

Instinct told him late the next day that a leader has to orient his personal life or he is ineffectual in leading; the lingering embarrassment of defeat in battle made it necessary to bolster his pride and confidence. But how? He gave thought to it, although his inner consciousness already knew the answer, the desire. He yearned for that comfort that a man gets only from a woman.

Forthwith he set out to find her. He did not go back to Luz Corral, or even wish to. Nor did he consider any of the camp followers, though some were pretty. Smiling a little at himself, he asked three of his closest remaining associates to "ride out with him for a few hours." They had no choice; curious anyway, they were willing. In due time the riders happened onto a peon sheepherder's home.

Pancho had not planned it so, indeed had planned nothing except vaguely to go searching for what he told himself would be "the right one." He didn't know where he'd find her, nor did he care. But as it happened, nine children were at the sheepherder's home, and next to the oldest was one of those ripely beautiful maidens such as only the hills of Mexico and the bloodstreams of the Indians can produce. Pancho's eyes brightened with the first real show of pleasure they had held since he heard the rattle of the machine guns.

"Ah, *señorita*, I like you very much," said he, forthwith.

She smiled her shy appreciation. He came close to her, put a hand on her shining black hair, looked closely at her ivory shoulders, arms, and face. "You will come with me now. We will be married at once. You know who I am? My name is Pancho Villa. It is good, eh, for us to fall in love?"

It was good. It was, from the parents' point of view, they being overwhelmed by a sudden gift of money and a proposal from such a magnificent man. Pancho fully understood their feelings; years ago he had lived their lives. It was good from her point of view, she who had dared hope only that some gentle ranch worker might in time take her to his arms. He liked her smile. So the horsemen rode away with the girl behind Pancho's saddle. He felt her clinging to him in wide-eyed excitement. The entire courtship had lasted barely half an hour.

Pancho had learned from the parents that a village was only six miles away, with a little church. They pointed toward that. The priest was found asleep in his study but he roused at once and greeted his important looking callers with considerable interest. When he heard Pancho's story, he nodded.

"You have never been married before, I assume?" said he.

Pancho shrugged and smiled. "Maybe. Who can say? But that is all past. Now I would marry this one."

"You have been divorced, then? The church does not countenance divorce, and especially remarriage after—"

"Who in the high hopping hell cares what the church thinks?" Pancho suddenly turned fierce. "Marry us, father. Now!"

The priest, a godly man, drew himself up in indignation. He would have commanded Pancho to leave his holy presence and stop desecrating the temple in which they stood. But abruptly his eyes were held by a shining pistol in Pancho's hand. "*Now*, father, if you wish to live!"

The ceremony was brief. If the good padre did not appreciate it, Pancho and his chuckling henchmen did. And the girl? That poor creature of the soil was as romantically eager as her lover was, Pancho observed happily. What is religion, he asked himself, when the pulse is pounding with desire? What are mumbled words at an altar when a human god has dropped out of the sky and lifted you literally off your feet?

The party "rested" in the village for twenty-four hours. Nobody disturbed the lovers except to bring them food. They had three rooms in a home confiscated for the purpose. If any one had dared creep close to door or window, colossal snorings would have been heard. Pancho knew that a woman and a long sleep can do much to restore a man who has just lost two battles.

When he came out on the second morning he felt and looked like a man drugged. Half staggering, he went to the well in the village plaza nearby and a native hastened to draw a bucket of water. Pancho motioned for the man to pour it over his head. Much sloshing, massaging, and sighing followed, but Pancho stood up greatly refreshed.

"Ah ha," said he, grinning now. "Is good, eh?"

"Yes sir," the villager nodded, still frightened of the man.

Almost immediately the four horsemen prepared to ride away again, but after they had mounted, Pancho turned his gelding back to the doorway where his bride was standing.

"Everything is fine, señora," said he, saluting her. He reached down to give her some golden coins. "Here, buy yourself something, eh? One of these days we visit again, maybe. You wait for Pancho. I am a soldier, you understand? I have much to do.

I cannot stay here making love. Adios."

She said nothing as he spurred away. About two hundred yards out he reined his horse, which reared dramatically and turned. Pancho waved to the girl and she waved back. He liked her; liked her very much, he told himself. But he never saw or heard of her again.

Two days later Pancho sat in his tent in his mountain lair considering anew the two military defeats that he had suffered. Inevitably he reached an old, significant conclusion: "I am too damned ignorant to be an army colonel. I have got to get out of this or I have got to learn more."

He summoned a friend in his command, Tomas Urbina.

"I had heard of machine guns, Tomas," said he. "Had you heard of them?"

"Yes, I had heard."

"Then why in the high hopping hell hadn't you warned me to get some of them, eh? I ought to have you shot. Tomas, you have sixty days to get me at least one hundred of those pop guns that fire like hail on a tin roof. And somebody to teach us how to operate them."

He knew where Urbina would get them. Already opportunists were trying to contact the new and spectacular "Tiger of the North" in Mexico. Most were Americans, he discovered. They wanted to provide his uniforms, foodstuffs, vehicles, rifles, horses, everything—for gold. Pancho understood that.

The defeats also made Pancho realize that he suffered from lack of advance information. He had sent out spies of a sort, to be sure. These had simply ridden to the top of the next hill or so, surveyed the enemy at long range, and reported back. Or they had depended on small-talk gossip picked up in *cantinas*, saloons, and whore houses. Pancho knew all this.

But no longer was it adequate. He gave thought to this one morning while moping there in his headquarters tent. He wanted high class service now, knew that such was imperative. Instinct told him that almost any Mexican would enjoy playing cloak-and-dagger because of the romantic twist inherent in his people, but he also knew that a real spy must have intelligence and discretion, plus unquestioned loyalty. He made a list of six men who might fill that need, then added two women.

He called the men to him, explained what he wanted, and sent

97

them out on their own. Then he called in the women and carefully briefed them, individually, on how to spy on his six male spies. They were to try to seduce the males and worm secret information out of them. "I will pay you well," he privately told each woman in turn.

"What will you pay?" one asked.

He considered that a moment, and a sure instinct served him well again. "I will marry you," said Pancho the Great, turning on his irresistible smile.

It was enough, he discovered. She was completely loyal—and so were all the others. Both females double-checked for him on the six males. Nobody turned traitor. In a few months the six men, with others subsequently added, developed a very effective secret service. Pancho was able to know the approximate size of the garrisons that defended a town he planned to attack, and to know where his enemies were at any given time. A simple bit of acting and a "secret" code system of communication was sufficient for this. He himself devised the code, and took a small boy delight in it.

Meanwhile, too, the Tiger of the North found that American adventurers had been lured to him by his growing legend of action and excitement. These men, by no means saintly, nevertheless felt a backwoodsy, masculine, daredevil sort of kinship with Pancho's ideal of liberating the poor people of Mexico. When he found this trait in them he couldn't turn them away; a pleasant sort of camaraderie developed between him and them, a drinking, yarn-telling, woman-loving companionship. He realized that a few of these leeches wanted their share of rebel loot, but in his hearty type of generosity he didn't begrudge them. Some were newspapermen, and Pancho again discovered that these were most valuable of all. They had insight, plus inside information; he was astonished to see how much a fellow called "Rube" Hopkins knew about everything going on in Mexico.

Rube, he learned, was a newshawk from Tucson, Arizona, with a long nose that not only sniffed out facts at long range but also retained, sorted, and classified them, as if in a file case ready for Pancho to pull out and study when needed. In some past center of activity he had left one of his legs as a souvenir so that he entered Villa's camp on crutches. Pancho took to him at once; any man one-legged, with guts enough to want to be a Villista, deserved a hearing. He soon justified Pancho's faith. Not only did he become wise counsel for the guerrilla leader, but when occasion arose he could hop around on one leg, reverse a crutch, and use it as a club to beat an enemy senseless. Between times, he furnished Pancho with that ingredient priceless in any serious drama, comic relief.

"Thoss Rube," Pancho would almost shout, in his version of English, "She ees the *mucho* fonny, hah! She ees tell from the girl whoos dress he fall off in frawnt from the preacher in the church, and thoss preacher she—WHOO-O-O!" He'd erupt in raucous laughter that could be heard all over the camp. He'd never finish the story, but he didn't need to; his American audience would dutifully laugh with him, and they had heard the old bawdy bit anyway. Such a fellowship built a loyalty. He had a brain trust, a "military staff," and he liked it so.

All in all, then, Pancho knew he was "ready" after a few more months had elapsed. Not only were his men better trained, he himself was. The privates in his army had been molded into a military machine, American style. He warned himself that he must not do impulsive attacking. Rather than just decide on the spur of the moment to rush madly into a town and try to take it by force, he shrewdly investigated first. In short, a new respect for efficiency developed in him; preparedness became a common-sense passion; strategy became as important a military concept as were obedience and marksmanship.

All this while he had been nursing a very special ambition, a goal, and by May of 1911 he felt ready to start. To insure the advantage of surprise, he told no one except his spies, not even his lieutenants. And so on command, his rejuvenated army swooped down to complete the disintegration of the Don Luis Terrazas ranch empire.

The episode began when soldiers—as distinguished now from rag-tag bandits—marched in carefully prepared pattern on the City of Juarez, Chihuahua. Anxious, wary in his heart, Pancho showed nothing but confidence, riding head high, smiling big. He directed the battle for all of one day and most of a night, the longest and most methodical that he had yet undertaken. Even so, the defenders outnumbered the Villistas. After a little more fighting Pancho began an apparently disorderly retreat, and this heartened the defending Federal leader, General Juan J. Navarro. He ordered an all-out charge to run down and kill every contemptible Villista. Pancho was delighted. Grinning, he sprung the trap he had prepared.

A few minutes after most of the Federals had dashed out to pursue Villa, his bugle blew not far away. It was like releasing a taut spring. From "nowhere," or apparently from hell itself, came an eruption of shouting, screaming, shooting cavalrymen, and the tenor of their terrorizing cries was *"VIVA VI-I-I-I-LLA-A-A-A!"*

They were morale breakers and bone breakers, they were centaurs spouting fire. The Federals, rushing to "victory," were overwhelmed. Even as the peon villagers had been during the bandit raids, they were awed by the huge man on the black horse who roared in at the head of the hellions. They saw him slashing with his colonel's sword, watched him dash into any little group engaged in hand-to-hand combat with bayonets and turn the tide, felt the impact of his strength and personality at every hand. Pancho himself was in his glory; this was the sort of fiery action that he loved.

He knew that he had never fought harder or more enjoyably than he did that 11th of May. He realized it was very personal with him; that he was not only fighting for a high ideal, the liberation of Mexican peons, but for the punishment of those who had made the liberation necessary. He knew this was a Terrazas town, and that it also was headquarters for many another arrogant *rico*. This fact, plus the ignominy of his recent defeats, were inspiration enough.

When the passion for killing had begun to subside and a semblance of order was restored, Colonel Villa began taking prisoners. Soon these were herded into groups like Terrazas cattle at shipping time. Pancho, eyeing them critically, rode among them, shrewdly choosing those who had been forced to fight. These he cut out, as a *vaquero* cuts out unbranded beasts at roundup, and made them a little speech. They were victims of slavery, of tyranny, he informed them, knowing they already knew that; he, Colonel Pancho Villa, had freed them. Would they now like to support Villa's cause to free all of Mexico? They would! He grinned and waved his sword in welcome as they cheered.

He was interrupted by a messenger saying that the defending General Navarro would like to surrender.

"Ha!" exclaimed Pancho to Tomas Urbina, his then close associate. "He would surrender, eh? What else can he do?"

What else indeed. But presently Pancho remembered that he himself was, after all, a military leader, a man of size and substance now. He could not be disdainful. He could not conduct himself as, say, that uncouth, murdering bandit Parra would have done. He was Colonel Francisco Villa, liberator of the people. Dignity must be observed. Therefore, he made the surrender a picture-book performance with much bowing, much extending of swords, much effusive courtesy and protocol.

Pancho happily discovered that the stores of Juarez were crowded to the rafters with rich merchandise. He knew this was because of proximity to the United States. Foods, textiles, utensils, clothing, household goods of every sort, automobiles, all manner of marvelous things such as only America has ever produced in the history of man, had made their way across the international bridges from El Paso. Pancho ordered his men to throw open the merchants' doors.

While the poor families of Juarez thus were acquiring overwhelming treasures, he watched his own trained supply sergeants confiscate whatever the Villistas needed. This soon amounted to boxcar loads, then train loads. General Navarro had neglected to destroy his arsenal, Pancho learned with glee. Ammunition and guns by the thousands thus were taken. Great warehouses of grain were welcomed; cavalry horses, moving with speed across country to liberate the poor, must eat. Hats, coats, underwear, sox, shoes, mess equipment, all the endless array of material that an army needs, could be gathered here. Pancho, beaming happily, seemed to be everywhere at once, directing the looting.

But on top of that, Pancho knew that *La Ciudad Juarez* was a northern center of banking. Don Luis Terrazas did most of his money handling here. So did many another wealthy man. Again the proximity to the United States was the reason, Pancho had guessed, for there was cooperation with the El Paso banks, and a cordial feeling of prosperity was maintained. To support all of this, bags of silver and gold had to be kept *some*where; the paper money of Mexico never was much respected in the minds of the people, whereas tangible metal coins had substance and strength. Pancho himself gave away only golden coins.

"We shall replenish the Madero treasury, eh?" Colonel Villa

now said to his subordinates. "Let there be no foolish destruction or killing over this—we shall screen out any undesirables later. Let us call on the Juarez banks in an orderly manner, eh?"

Call on the banks. It could be interesting; it could be fun. Not one in a thousand of these Villistas had ever been inside any bank's doors. How does one "call on a bank?" Pancho himself had never had an occasion to enter a bank. But it was common knowledge among peons that banks had unlimited money, so presumably they made the stuff. Money didn't grow on trees, eh?

Pancho took none of these ignorant, loyal men with him. He took the knowledgeable ones, the *Americanos* who had shown most "*savvy*" while riding with him. To back them he took a picked squad of quick-trigger aides, followed by loyal and willing burden bearers.

The banker had foreseen the possibility that Villa might take the city after first news of the attack, so he had done his duty to his depositors as best he could. He had reasoned that, if the city fell, Villistas would surely come to inspect the bank vaults. They did so come—and found them empty.

"How is that, *señor?*" demanded Pancho. "No money is here. Why?"

"Ah, Colonel Villa, we were raided by the despised Federals just before you came. They took every *peso* and *centavo*."

"Think of that!" exclaimed Villa, enjoying a bit of lofty sarcasm. "You would have saved it for me if possible? You are friends of those who bring freedom to Mexico?"

The banker, a vice-president, bowed graciously. "To be sure, sir. Your cause is our cause. It is in teamwork that we must effect *la libertad* for all."

Pancho Villa's great mouth opened in bullish, masculine laughter. "You are a lying son of a dog, *señor*, you know it and I know it. OYEZ! Pascual, find the money! And you—" he designated a corporal in his escorting squad, "see that *el señor* is taken care of, eh? You will know where to take him."

The mop-up crew found the money, some $400,000 in Mexican and American specie. One husky, mahogany-skinned soldier, whose muscles had been developed as a blacksmith on a ranch, actually discovered it. They had searched inside without encouragement, so he swung a huge pile-driving hammer at one of those impressive columns that adorned the front of the bank. The

102

column appeared to be of stone but was actually of hollow plaster. When his fourth blow tore off a big section, coins fell to the sidewalk in a golden cascade.

11

COLONEL FRANCISCO VILLA heard himself called by that full name and title for the next few days in Juarez. He felt elated, tried to act dignified but couldn't quite manage it, and realized his own shortcoming. He thought once to abandon the name Francisco Villa entirely.

"After all," he even addressed himself one morning, in the mirror of a Juarez hotel he had made into temporary headquarters, "I am not Francisco Villa, I am Doroteo Arango . . . Colonel Arango, eh? Teo Arango. *Viva Arango.*"

He scowled a bit at that. It didn't sound good; not nearly as good as "Viva Villa." The Teo was as good a nickname as Pancho, he felt; he could make intimate friends with that. But the Arango had a twang to it, and Villa sounded better. He liked the way his men strung it out in their battle cry—*vee-e-e-e-e-yah-h-h-h.* No, he'd best not change his name again; Pancho Villa he'd remain.

The sudden new respect shown him was interesting, too, he decided. Much of it was actual subservience; peons backed away from him, bowing. He tried to be genial Pancho, but they wanted Colonel Villa. They were making him important, whereas he thought of himself as a junior soldier serving under Madero and Orozco; the small frog in the big puddle, he tried to tell his aides. Even they would have none of it. They solemnly assured him that he was the biggest new influence on Mexican politics. He didn't understand that at all, although he said nothing. More and more in recent months he was conscious of his ignorance in many areas.

But he knew he had a Cause, and that he was also having fun.

"Is good we be *conquistadores*, eh my fran's?" he asked American newspapermen, happily, in his version of their language.

"You're a conqueror, all right, Colonel," one said.

103

"We make the beeg—how you say heem?—los head marks? By the top of the—the—*periodico*."

"Head*lines*, sir, in the *newspapers*. Say, you're doing all right with your English!"

"I espeak heem good. *¿No es verdad? Bueno*, I espeak heem all the tam. I be educate. Maybe I become a *gringo* myselves and make love to the *gringo señori*—the *gringo* gurr-r-rls." He gave it a Scottish burr, straining for perfection. "They onderstan' me. They have much beauty, the esmiles, the—the oh-you-keed, eh?" He laughed heartily. He fancied himself quite a companion for the news correspondents and, in point of fact, was.

In turn, his own feeling for them was not quite of friendship, in the deep meaning of that term, but of comradeship. He accepted them as pals, knowing they might be useful in recreational pursuits as well as in building public opinion in his favor. But he made it clear that he wasn't dependent on them. They could make a place for themselves in his favor or they could get the hell out. One brash chap wrote a piece which called him "the most dastardly bandit ever to arise in Mexico." An educated rebel got a copy of the paper in Nogales, Arizona, and sent it to Pancho with a translation. Pancho had this read to him then called the reporter to his tent.

"Well, well, my friend," he spoke his usual Spanish in greeting him, knowing that all the reporters were bilingual. "I have here a paper saying I am a *dastard*. You are a younger man than I am, so I take care of your morals like a big brother.

"I do not want you to be associated with a dastard bandit. So, I send you home to mama."

"But Pancho! Colonel Villa! You understand it was not—"

"Do not talk. The more you talk, the more trouble you get into. I tell you what—I help you back to the United States. You start out of the camp right now. I encourage you."

As if by magic his two famous Colt .45's materialized in his hands. Pancho was not smiling. The reporter wasted no time.

Pancho emptied his pistols, not at the man—whom he might easily have killed if he had wished to—but at the ground just a few feet ahead of his running form. *POW! Zing!* Bullets ricochetted off rocks with musical rhythm. Pancho laughed uproariously. Witnessing correspondents judiciously laughed with him. When he had reloaded and reholstered, he said to them, in their

tongue again, "Me, I am a son of a beech, eh? Beeg son of beech."
They laughed again; nervously.

It was these same newsmen, he realized, who best kept him
informed about his political ascendancy.

"President Diaz is having plenty of trouble with people who
want his job," they'd say.

"Of course," Pancho thought he understood fully. "General
Madero."

"And that man Huerta."

"Huerta? Who is he, my friends?"

"Victoriano Huerta. An Indian. But a commissioned officer in
the army of President Diaz. *He* wants to be president," they said.
"He might even make it; if you and Madero don't stop him."

"He would make a *good* president? He would be a friend to
the peons? If he was a poor Indian himself—"

"Don't bank on it, Colonel. The worst oppressors of the poor
are likely to be those who once were poor themselves."

Pancho didn't understand that. He sat up straight, holding a
glass of *agua miel* which he was drinking. "What about me?
I am from the poor people, and I do not seek to oppress them."

"There has never been but one Pancho Villa," they reminded
him, smiling.

He learned, therefore, as he fought. The bigger he got, the
broader he grew in knowledge. He was no longer an overgrown
boy with a pistol robbing to help his poverty-ridden mother, he
told himself. Now he was colonel of a very powerful regiment
of rebels, men not drafted or forced to fight but inspired by
abundant food and a glimpse of freedom. He had become a
national figure even in his enemies' eyes, and knowledge of this
set him frowning.

He was glad when Madero was elected president in 1911 and
Diaz was forced to flee. He didn't understand how yet another
aspirant, an Indian named Victoriano Huerta, could arise as a
traitor to Madero's cause. He wasn't really much interested, he
tried to explain; he wanted simply to retire on a ranch, to a form
of living which would have made him comfortable and quiet in
the company of trusted friends. Why not? His man Madero was
elected. What more had he, Pancho, actually to do? He asked
that often, of his associates.

One day soon after Madero's election he rode back to his lawful wife Luz Corral de Villa. He had not actually seen much of Luz. Their marriage had not been a long-considered thing, though it was not an act of force or passion. The wedding ceremony had been performed by a priest in the little town of San Andres on October 17, 1909, when the Rurales and the rich ranchers' police and even the Federal militia were actively hunting for Pancho Villa. He could not stay near his Luz long, lest he be captured. After that, he had been much too busy to linger around her.

But now with Madero elected, he felt that possibly he and she might settle down together. The thought appealed to him, and he outlined it to her in some detail, envisioning a newer, quieter happiness.

"So many things you do not know, my Pancho," Luz murmured, when he paused for her answer. He saw that she was crocheting a lace collar, so dainty that it reminded him of the silver filigree of Mexican jewelry.

"How is that? I can get what I do not now have. If you wish for something that is hard to find, I will hunt for it." He reached out to touch the lace collar appreciatively. He felt a yearning, for home.

"Hush." She was gentle with it. "I want for little, and need less. I was not thinking of myself. I was thinking of you."

He looked at her for a long moment, watching the speed of her fingers and needle, the consummate grace, the beauty and skill. His brow had furrowed a little.

"Pancho, you are very loyal to President Madero."

"Certainly, yes."

"Do you not know that General Pascual Orozco of the Madero forces, your own ally—did you not once say your own commander?—is now 'secretly' on the other side?"

Colonel Villa sat up. "What are you saying, woman?"

"Remember, I am a merchant's daughter. I listen and I learn much. Unlike many women, I do not gabble all afternoon and evening, but I do not miss what is going on."

"Orozco, the swine! He has never liked me."

She looked straight at him now. "You know that much at least, so? It is true. Nor has he liked Madero. General Orozco is a man to take care of General Orozco first and last. Pancho, jealousy can be a horrid thing."

106

"What do you mean by his being on the 'other side'?"

"He is the new chief of the military zone of Chihuahua, that's what I mean. And as such is a leader in a new insurrectionist movement to kick President Madero out."

"Hell and damnation, we just put Madero in! Orozco helped do it!" He was standing now, the warrior again.

The woman shrugged. "You have to learn about traitors *some-where*, my Pancho. Go and learn the way a man likes to learn—from other men. Go and hear the truth about Orozco from your own spies; though the talk of a happy life on a quiet ranch, Pancho—" She had stopped her needle, and she sighed now with an obvious yearning of her own, before she looked up at him and went on. "It is not to be. Not likely soon. You have a destiny, Pancho. You will be riding, you will again be shouting and shooting, you will be a comet leaving its trail of fire across the Mexican sky."

Young Colonel Villa said no more to her. He felt saddened, confused, but angry, too. He began slowly walking to her door, his mind leaping far ahead; she had ceased to exist for him.

Orozco. The son of a swine, Orozco. It was true about him, he could be sure, for it was like him. A traitor, whose hand hadn't yet been publicly revealed. Then it was well that he, Pancho Villa, knew it. Many things would have to be done.

He was barely back at his own headquarters when messengers from Madero confirmed what Luz had told him. Orozco, the swine. Pancho sent the presidential envoys back with a message saying that he would die if necessary to defend the government of Madero, who had been in office only since November 5, 1911. It might truly be necessary to die, he realized. Orozco would fight. He was a vindictive, bloodthirsty, military man who would seek to kill every Villista in the land, and Pancho well knew it. He sighed hard, thinking of that. He would have to fight Orozco not as a centaur impressing the few defenders on a ranch, but with the cold science of warfare. Pancho knew that he was not equipped to do it, either in temperament, men or materiel.

To his dismay, he soon learned that, in the City of Chihuahua, Orozco had taken all the Madero troops under his command. Because men's minds are flexible, Orozco had bent most of them his way. Pancho understood that technique; he used it himself.

Orozco used it in 1912. Hundreds who heard, never lived to learn that Orozco had lied. Pancho saw that their bodies turned a little green, and that the vultures were bloated from over-eating though they mostly just pecked out such choice morsels as the eyes, before clean-up men after the battle got all the burying or burning done. Nevertheless, their side, Orozco's side, had won.

To save the life that he had vowed to give if need be, Pancho Villa fled like the erstwhile bandit. He felt no shame from the fleeing. He was not a whipped dog, tail tucked and body cringing, crawling off to tremble and whine. He was a strategist fleeing to recoup his forces and attack again. Even as he retreated he issued a command that was passed from man to man all down his lines:

"Separate today and do not be captured. Ten nights from now come quietly to meet me at our hideout in the Chihuahua hills. The Villistas will ride again!"

12

Pancho took momentary pleasure at being back in his mountain lair. He rode up the wild free slopes with admiration for them, because they were his homeland, and he felt a kinship here. The stay in plush luxury in Juarez had palled quickly; a man, a he-man, wants little of that, he realized anew.

But he found scant time for enjoying the wilderness; responsibility had ridden close behind him. Accepting it, he felt his mood turning sullen and vicious. He didn't like that, but he couldn't do anything about it, or thought he couldn't. A companion had betrayed him, then defeated him in battle.

Out of the saddle and back at his camp desk—a crude table thing set up by his aides—he still felt low, low. He knew that a lesser man would have taken it out in drunkenness. Pancho Villa never was victimized by alcohol; he rarely even smoked. On this morning in camp, therefore, he simply paced, and snarled at orderlies, or at any one who crossed him even slightly. He knew he was being mean, and for the moment, didn't care. He had to think.

"You should eat something besides meat for dinner, Colonel," a solicitous captain suggested kindly, noting Pancho's menu that second night in camp.

With the ferocity of a madman—which momentarily he was—Pancho threw the entire platter into the captain's face and ordered him from the tent. If the captain had offered so much as a hint of protest at this treatment, he would have been shot instantly.

Half an hour later, Pancho sought out the under officer and said, "I am dung from a dog, captain. You are right, a man needs food besides meat. He needs a lot of things. He needs guts. He needs help to whip Orozco, the son of a swine! I apologize, captain. You are my friend. Oyez—you!" This last was directed at a private who by chance was near. "Bring a platter of raw meat at once. Here."

"Ra—raw meat, Colonel?" The private looked his astonishment.

"*Raw meat!* Bloody raw meat! From the kitchens. Before I make raw meat of you!"

The private was back with it in scarcely a minute; cuts of beef, ready for tomorrow's stew. Pancho took the platter and forced it into his captain's reluctant hands. "Now," he ordered, deadly serious. "You shall have your revenge. Captain—right in my face."

The captain begged not to. He tried to laugh it off. He held the meat as if it were scorching him, and did everything in his power to end the fantastic scene, but in the end he had to obey. He threw the cuttings all over his commander. He expected virtually anything to result from it—a quick death perhaps would have been the easiest bounty. But Pancho Villa only shook himself, said "Now we are both damn fools," and went away to clean himself.

That same evening, he discovered, his dozen close under-officers brought the girls who "leveled" Pancho.

The men had known what to do, he realized in some embarrassment. He knew that they had already sent couriers to four or five villages with instructions to quietly spread a romantic word—"Pancho Villa is lonesome. He would welcome any friendly young woman who might care to visit him. He would give her gold. And in camp with him are many other handsome men, too. You understand?"

Plenty did understand, it appeared. It apparently had been no trouble at all to round up thirty who were virginal at least in appearance. Pancho studied them quietly. They had dressed their best—none too good in most cases, but colorful and clean. He appreciated their cleanliness, their feminine fragrance. Musicians were found among the soldiers, guitars and banjos, horns and drums soon formed into what passed for an orchestra.

By 9 o'clock that evening a small box canyon near Pancho's tent had taken on festive atmosphere. A hundred or more torches fashioned from resinous woods of the mountains had been stuck into the ground or on the rocks, outlining the canyon like *luminarias* around a cathedral during Christmas celebration. Breeze was just enough to give life to the flames.

The beginning was as ingratiating as moonlight. Indeed it was *about* moonlight—a crooning, soft and seductive, with an ever-so-gentle touch of string chords behind it, barely audible at first but moving closer, its words promising achievement far removed from wars—

> *The moon is a flower of heaven,*
> *Its petals strewn over the world;*
> *The night is a garden of glory*
> *For any young man and his girl.*

Thus Pancho heard the siren song of the evening, a folk ballad calling all to lay aside frettings and fumings and share happiness with friends.

At his desk he stood up, listening, then before his orderly could move he himself threw back the tent flaps. Nine of the maidens were approaching under torchlight, softly crooning and smiling, looking at him with bright, welcoming eyes. The big man's face broke into the first smile of happiness it had shown in days. He stepped outside, stood feet wide apart, fists on hips, staring at the vision of loveliness. Guitars spoke gently from the background while the girls sang, and now and then male voices came in with bass, tenor, and baritone. Presently Pancho himself was keeping the rhythm with his head, swaying a little, succumbing to the mood of the music. When the song ended and all the girls were laughing, he stepped closer to them.

"*Maravilloso!*" he exclaimed, and bowed like a Spanish grandee.

Because a guitar was still carrying the waltz rhythm he put an arm around the nearest maiden and began to dance with her.

He swung her grandly, lifting her from her feet, loving her and laughing gaily with her while the orchestra and singers picked up the music again. Presently they marched away as if by spoken command, leading him and the girl down a little slope, around some boulders into the lighted, flat canyon area. He hardly spoke at all. He accepted the astonishing fiesta for the bounty that it was, unexpected but *maravilloso* indeed.

With thirty excited girls and many times more that number of eager men, the party lasted right on through to exhaustion. The canyon floor had been picked clean of most sticks and stones, Pancho observed. For one accustomed all his youth to dancing in adobe dwellings or simply under the sky, this floor was excellent. The tempo became livelier as the hours passed. Pancho never seemed to tire; he enjoyed the endless, happy screechings and gigglings that were testimonials to his enthusiasm. Yet, some time after midnight, he realized that he had been stirred most by a pretty creature who wore a cluster of wild mountain flowers over one ear. He never asked her name—nobody here this night seemed to have a name, or to care, everybody acted as if acquainted from childhood. All the camp officers had joined in, Pancho discovered, as had many of the non-commissioned ones, and even some of the favored privates. Those who did not quite dare to step out into the dancing, at least sang and swayed and clapped hands on the sidelines, some stationed a hundred feet or more up the sides of the cliffs. Their colonel told himself that this was all to the good; that his men had been needing a time of recreation.

At 2 a.m. or so, Pancho led Señorita Flowers-in-the-Hair quietly away. He knew he had to offer no explanation. They were seen no more until nearly noon, when breakfast was served to them on a table in the warming sunshine outside his tent. He felt calm, peaceful.

He knew that before dawn each of the girls had paired off with some one. Smiling, he wondered how the pairing was done. He learned that four or five fights developed over the matter—quiet challenges, with quick fist blows and the thrust of a dagger or two. From these, two men ultimately died. No matter; fiesta is fiesta, Pancho mentioned, and men have always fought over girls. It is a shame, yet it is to be expected, eh *señor?*

The fact that Colonel Villa drank no liquor did not set a precedent for his men. He noticed that fiery *tequila* had flowed. As

111

always, it begat a certain boisterousness, but fortunately this had swelled around the rocks away from Pancho's tents and did not disturb him.

With intermittent sleeping, eating, drinking, singing, dancing, and some fighting interspersed, the fiesta continued well into the following afternoon.

At midday when Pancho and his no-longer-virginal maiden were finishing breakfast, a dozen or so of the merrymakers dared serenade them again. Satiated, he smiled a welcome. Their song was one that he knew and liked, *La Cucaracha*, the cockroach.

Men and girls here in the mountain camp began to vie with one another making up verses for it.

> *La cucaracha, la cucaracha,*
> *He has no hairs upon his ugly head.*
> *La cucaracha, la cucaracha,*
> *Takes every girl he can into his bed.*

That was one bit of impromptu lyrics which seemed to please the merrymakers most, Pancho noted, laughing uproariously with them. Dozens more stanzas were created (then hundreds, down through the years). La *cucaracha* metamorphosed from a repulsive thing scurrying about garbage, into any devil-may-care lover or adventurer who happened to adorn the Mexican scene. Pancho personally came to know several dozen stanzas of the ballad, many of them his own. (Ultimately it achieved renown as the theme song of the Villista army.)

The fiesta ended by the second midnight, and on the following morning Pancho was his old self again. He arose at dawn eager for work. Most of the girls stayed in the camp for a week or more, some sticking with the soldiers for months, but Pancho was scarcely aware of them after his hearty celebration.

Somewhat to his surprise, he had more than five hundred men when he counted noses in his mountain hideout. He had hoped for two hundred, maybe three, but here was a strong force of his regulars plus many recruits, each man well mounted and well armed. Best of all, the new ones were eager volunteers, he discovered; they had not joined him on sudden impulse, swayed by banners and applause, nor for expediency as he rode into them a conqueror. They had traveled long distances and endured hardships because the name Pancho Villa was still magic. He was touched, emotional about it. He found his able sergeants, lieutenants, and captains, and embraced them. Some of the Americans who had fought with him or at least stayed close by, had guessed where he would be. These showed up, grinning, at the breakfast tents. He bade them welcome. Then he ordered all soldiers to resume the conditioning drills in the valleys and to sharpen up their skill with bayonets and bullets.

One day Pancho faced that most shining of all devils—Temptation. He rode into the Sierra as a courier with a rifle, but it was held high and a white flag was tied to the bayonet. That got him near to Colonel Villa's tent.

"It is an *old* man, sir," his orderly advised Pancho.

"Old? What does he want? Give him a gold coin or two and bid him go. I have work to do."

"He insists that he has a message from General Orozco."

"That contemptible son of a dog!" Villa jumped from his chair, eyes flashing, lips taut, jaw thrust out. "Bring him in here. And stand to one side when you do, if you would not be accidentally killed."

Alone, Pancho fought to control his wrath; a colonel must not be a fool, he told himself. He flexed his muscles, tensed them, then relaxed. But he must not show weakness, either. In a few moments, there inside the tent flaps was truly an old man. Pancho glared at him. But he was *too* old. One does not shoot a patriarch if he has come fearlessly to you, even though he be from an enemy.

"I am General Orozco's father," the messenger said, calmly.

That bold statement had its effect. Pancho admired courage.

"I had thought to shoot you at once," Pancho said.

The old man nodded. "Sooner or later, someone will." (Someone did. Orozco's father was shot the following year by the southern general Emiliano Zapata, when on a similar mission.) "My son would trust no one else with his message. He does not care if I am killed."

Colonel Villa sat back down. Curiosity had him now. "State your message," he ordered. "Make it brief."

"I understand; where perhaps my son does not. As you know, he heads the new revolution. He wants you to desert Madero and join him. If you will do that, Orozco will pay you immediately three hundred thousand pesos. That is all."

Villa stared long at him. Once three hundred thousand pesos would have seemed a mountainous amount. Now he, Pancho Villa, could take vaster sums on his own. He spat, to show his contempt.

"Tell your despicable son I shall personally cut his testes out at the earliest opportunity. And that I shall make the opportunity soon." It was a happy thought. The father made no comment. "For yourself, old one, know that I am in this fight because of my feelings and not for any personal gain. Your swine of a son will not understand that, but I think you may be a wiser man. The government of President Madero was the result of a free election. It is my duty and my pleasure to fight against traitors. Now go before I take out my anger on you."

Pancho soon discovered that other traitors were developing. More and more his sense of confusion concerning national affairs was a burden to him. "Those politeeks, *amigos*, I do not onderstan' heem," he'd say to his *Americano* friends. "W'at good they do, eh?"

"It's because everybody wants something for himself, Colonel," one tried to explain. "Just like Huerta down here—*he* wants to be head man, and he'll cut throats to get there."

Pancho understood that all too well. "Son of a beech," he growled. "He now *my* boss! Me, Pancho Villa!"

The American shrugged. "President Madero made him head of the Federal army. So in effect he is your commander-in-chief. And he hates your guts."

"Well, why?" Pancho was indignant, and curious.

"Well, for one thing, you don't drink much, and he's a damned drunkard. The hard drinker invariably despises a man who will not drink."

"Hah!" Disgust showed on Pancho.

"He always dresses in precise military costume and expects all around him to do so. But you, Colonel, you run around in picturesque charro clothes. How about that?"

Pancho grinned, flashing Rooseveltian teeth; he had seen pictures of Teddy Roosevelt, had been told much about that go-getter statesman, and had come to admire him. "Me, I am more handsome as a *caballero*, *señor*. The gur-r-rls like eet, eh?"

"But that doesn't butter your bread with Huerta. You are subject to his orders, and they won't be benevolent ones."

Within a month Pancho was ordered to head the new Federals, the Madero forces, in rapier-like thrusts at the traitorous Orozco.

Actually, he welcomed that, and he did the job with consummate skill. First he led his men at Tiahualilo. He prepared them both physically and emotionally, so that the sabre-swinging Villistas became a steel trap that caught the Orozco force in its jaws. Orozco himself barely escaped. Pancho saw his men enjoy a bloody field day of stabbing and shooting and shouting "VIVA VI-I-I-LLA-A-A!" over and over again.

It was much the same way at Conejos and Rellano. Pancho, flushed with success, learned from prisoners that Orozco was a living fury; the man Orozco had tempted to become a traitor like himself, now was whipping him at every turn, was magnificently defending the people's government of Madero. For reward, Colonel Villa was made brigadier general, by direct order of Huerta.

"Congratulations," an American reporter shook hands with him heartily one morning. "You are the headline maker of the continent."

"The whose?"

The American smiled. "The big news, sir, everywhere. Your stock is soaring. You know what the kids in the United States are saying now? When one meets another he says 'Hi, Pancho!' It's a compliment, to you. It's like calling a pal 'Buffalo Bill.' Even the college boys are doing it. In my country right now, if you ask a young man how he's feeling today, he is likely to say 'Viva Villa!' meaning he feels on top of the world."

Villa grinned big. "Is good, *no es verdad, Si*, I like him. Is—how you say?—pop'lar. *General* Villa—hah! Is good."

The American smiled genially again. "*Si.* Popular with everybody except Orozco. And Victoriano Huerta. I don't think you believe yet that Huerta is really your enemy as well as your boss."

Pancho shrugged. "He the big general. Me, the little one. Is bad?"

It came as a shock, then, to be brought up sharp in his unwonted conflict with the commander. One day after the three victories, Pancho went down with a cold. He did not take it philosophically. He was not sick enough to be in bed but was too sick to feel good, and was furious with the whole, frustrating

115

business. He had doctors on call. These gentlemen told him just to be cautious and within two weeks he would be well. For that he called them quacks and charlatans, and sent them scurrying. Then he called his orderlies in.

"Make me a small house, a tent, anything nearly air-tight, no bigger than this," he ordered measuring with his hands. "I want just room to sit in it beside a tub of water."

"You wish to bathe, my general?" one asked. "I will prepare—"

"You will do exactly as I say, or wish you had! Room for me and a tub of water."

"Yes sir!"

"Build a fire, put smooth stones the size of your head in it and heat them near to bursting. When they are ready, call me."

At the right time he stripped naked and went into his little house—they had hastily made it of rocks and mud, having at last realized what he wanted, and being entirely familiar with the custom. They brought two of the hot stones and dropped them into the tub, lowered the door curtain and waited his call. Presently they brought more hot stones to replace the cooled ones. Altogether he stayed in there two hours, steaming. Next day Pancho was completely well.*

While he lay on his cot to rest after that enervating steaming, a messenger came to him. "General Huerta wishes you to report to his headquarters at once, sir."

"I cannot come," Pancho dismissed him with a wave of hand. "Tell the old—tell the general that General Villa says he is sick and unable to report today."

Tomorrow came, and Pancho felt virile and vibrant again. He remembered the summons so he went to Huerta's tent. Recognized, of course, by the sentries and aides, Brigadier General Villa was ushered in immediately.

"Villa," the commander-in-chief drove straight to his point, "You are charged with thievery and insubordination."

Pancho's chin dropped. "How is that, sir?"

"You took a mare out of my stable without my permission. Then I sent for you and you refused to come."

---

*While it is scientifically probable that not one single cold virus was even annoyed by the steaming, *something* worked, exactly as it has seemed to work for primitive Mexicans and Indians who have so steambathed over the centuries. Possibly the rest helped as much as the steam.

"I took no mare, I am no thief!" General Villa almost shouted in his indignation. "And I was sick in bed when you ordered me to report. I came as soon as I could."

"That's a lie. You had just been having a bath. Besides—"

"No man calls Pancho Villa a liar!"

"*I* call you one. *Guard!*"

Two soldiers with rifles stepped out, bayonets fixed. Villa was appalled. He was actually being threatened.

"You are under arrest, Villa, for thievery and for disobeying me. The punishment is clear. You will be shot."

Pancho couldn't believe it. He was stricken numb. He had come here in a happy mood, even with a feeling of cordiality toward Huerta, his superior in command. A brigadier general may indeed have fellowship with a full general, he had assumed, for their ranks are close; yet technically there was a dividing line and Huerta had taken full advantage. Stunned as he was by the suddenness of it, Pancho couldn't draw his famous .45's to fight his way out of the trap, for the guards' rifles were cocked and their bayonets were inches from his chest. Within the half hour he was in the village of Jiminez, once more behind bars, livid with fury.

His hands remained tied behind him all day and all night. Dawn had barely begun to gild the skies when he heard the measured tramp-tramp-tramp of a squad approaching, heard the command "*AL-TO!*" A key rattled in the cell door, rusted hinges squeaked. Two men entered, each took an arm and jerked him to his feet. At bayonet point again he marched down the corridor and into the jail courtyard. A few rods away was an adobe wall. They stood him before it and took out a blindfold. Pancho looked around. Some fifteen or twenty military men, many of high rank, had gathered to see the Tiger of the North executed.

"I am innocent!" he cried out to them in despair. "By the Holy Virgin, why am I going to be shot?"

It was not fear that panicked him, he had always held a stoic indifference to death. Pancho was in despair at the injustice of his arrest and at the fact that he left much unfinished business. He knew his star had been rising again, he was strengthening Madero's cause by defeating the traitor Orozco. Thus it was maddening to be shot by his own commander-in-chief.

In that vein he made earnest plea to the assembled dignitaries. Long ago he had learned that, although he lacked formal educa-

117

tion, he did not lack an ability to talk. He had lately heard himself called one of the greatest speech makers Mexico ever knew. So now he truly opened his heart, and his every utterance seemed somehow to reach out and capture the people, as he argued with all the conviction and persuasion he could summon, suggesting that his summary execution this way could indeed have serious repercussions.

Hope leaped in him when he saw that he had captured the officers in command. Two times they sent messengers back to General Huerta, who had not deigned to witness the murder himself. These urged him to rectify the order for Villa's death. Each time Huerta refused, insisting that the execution be carried out.

"Very well," Pancho said, resigned. "Let me do one last thing, then. These men who must do the shooting—they are poor, as I was. I have some valuables with me. A gold watch. Some gold coins. Would you allow my hands to be untied?" He looked at the captain in command.

Why not? The captain, a very reluctant officer here anyway, agreed. Pancho, hands free, gave his personal effects to the soldiers he had commanded, men who looked into his eyes with horror at what they had been ordered to do.

"Do not fail," said he. "Shoot to kill, as I would have commanded you to do. I order you to do it now, on me. Your own lives depend on it—we all know that.

"For you, Juanito, the golden coins to take home to your Carmencita and your babies. For you, Estevan, my charro *pantalones;* you are not married, and you will cut a figure at the *baile,* eh? Kiss the prettiest ones in memory of me. For you, Sergeant Larriva, my gem-studded belt. Tell all of our men that I said they are to follow Madero. And if one has opportunity to slip his knife between the ribs of the man who will still command them for a while, the black-faced and black-hearted Huerta—" he nodded, knowingly.

He would have talked on, making the most of his last moments, but two horsemen galloped up. He turned to them.

They were Lieutenant Colonel Rubio Navarrete and Colonel Raoul Madero, brother of the president. Their arrival was like the climax in one of the cheap stage dramas he had seen as a very young man. It was impossible, it was unreal. He stared at them, open-mouthed, trying to assimilate it all, as one of them spoke.

"A telegram," said Colonel Madero brusquely, extending the paper to the officer in command. "The execution is stayed. General Villa is to be sent to Mexico City for trial before a military court."

It was so. Madero had wired his brother the president, and the answer had come in dramatic nick of time.

Pancho, numb with relief, soon found himself being taken under heavy guard to the Mexico City Penitentiary. Later he was transferred to the Santiago Military Prison nearby.

President Madero made it clear that he was not in sympathy with Huerta's summary treatment of Villa, yet the president could not arbitrarily countermand Huerta's orders without great risk, Pancho was told. The regime was shaky at best, and everything possible must be done to obey the established law and maintain orderly government.

Pancho tried hard to understand all that had happened, including Madero's motives. Again the awareness of his own limitations assailed him, his ignorance was an eternal curse, and turned always into confusion. But one thing was sharply clear.

"Say to the president," he pleaded with the messenger, "that Huerta is no more loyal to him than he had been to Diaz. Huerta is dog's dung. He is loyal to nobody but Huerta."

13

As MIGHT have been expected—if the guards in Mexico City had ever ridden with Pancho Villa or known much about him first hand—their distinguished prisoner was not a passive one, not one to be treated lightly. True, the power of rifle and bayonet is profound. But Pancho knew about other, subtler influences. Ridicule, for instance, which makes a guard a little ashamed to hide behind a gun. And persuasion. Also a man's overall ingratiating personality and poise. Pancho Villa used these inborn assets at every opportunity while he languished behind bars.

He didn't have many opportunities at first. He was held strictly incommunicado in the cold and dismal prisons. His "trial" became a farce, for not one shred of proof against him could be mustered. Still he was held, because Huerta's influence was just that strong. Four months passed. The cockroaches invading his cell numbered 1,069, Pancho reported years later, for he had personally counted them. That statistical report, of course, could have been inaccurate, he admitted, chuckling at the memory; cockroaches are nomadic by nature, like some tribes of Indians, and many could simply have been passing through on their way from other cells. There were nine hundred and forty steel rivets visible from Pancho's cell, inside and out. This figure is accurate to the rivet, for he counted them morning, noon, and night each day for one hundred and twenty-two days. It took seventeen steps to bring the jailer from the corridor entrance to his cell door.

On prison food such as his, a man in his thirties can progress from twenty push-ups at a time, lying face down and stiff, using only his arm muscles, to forty-four. Pancho took his exercises religiously. He would squeeze the cell window bars endlessly, strengthening hand and wrist muscles. He could keep knees straight and bend down to lay his palms flat on the floor. His belly, given at times to rotundity, became knotted with muscles instead of fat. His biceps bulged. His shoulders looked like advertisements on the backs of cheap magazines luring youths to send in money for body building courses. A part of this physical development was aided and abetted, it must be confessed, by Pancho's personal charm. He hadn't been in his cell three days before his jailers were slipping him extra, more palatable, and more nourishing food. But they could do nothing about the monotony, the boredom, the injustice.

One day he was driven by desperation to do something for himself. He had been escorted, as a part of routine, to the jail bath. After leaving the bath door, Pancho the strong, Pancho the handsome, looked at the turnkey and said, "Listen, sir, I am not going back to that cell."

The turnkey was indignant. After all, he had authority. "Who says you aren't going back? Why aren't you?"

"Because you treat people worse than you treat beasts. I haven't been allowed to have a lawyer, or even to speak with any outsider for months. I am innocent, sir. Bear in mind that I have not been convicted or sentenced. I am still being held for 'trial.' A mockery, sir. So I have decided to put an end to this outrage."

The turnkey, impressed, nevertheless was a man of some spirit in his own right. "So you're not going back!"

"No sir."

"That we shall see."

He hurried away then returned with four herculean guards, each carrying guns. Pancho awaited them with arms folded, and he was smiling cordially. "You may put me back," said he, "but you will have to kill me first."

"We can easily do that," said the turnkey now.

"Of course. But my friends—think! It would not be a happy thing for people outside to know that you gentlemen killed Pancho Villa, eh? A man who has fought all his life to help the poor, such as you? Your own friend? A friend of all who would see freedom and justice in Mexico? I am no weakling, either. True, you have guns. But I have strength, and one or more of you is likely to suffer severe—but no, let us not think of that. Let us remember what is right. Let us consider that three months in jail without so much as a chance to be heard—do you blame me, my friends, for this rebellion? Do you blame me for vowing to die before returning to that stinking cell?"

They were impressed. Pancho, touched with persuasive genius, had reached out once more. They left him and reported to Octaviano Liceago, the warden. He showed up a few minutes later and tried to persuade the guerrilla to obey. Pancho refused point blank.

The warden shrugged. "Stay in the hall, then, Villa, while I consult my superiors."

Pancho waited. He was playing for time, watching, alert. Later in the day Liceago reported that he had been ordered to end Villa's "solitary." The prisoner now could have freedom of the corridors and even walk some in the courtyard sun. Best of all, he had contact with other prisoners. Rapidly his influence began to be felt, he observed.

But his superiors saw that influence, too. Exactly four months after his entry into Mexico City, he was transferred to the military prison at Santiago Tlalteloco. Here, it apparently was reasoned, he would be an unknown, he could not arouse any disturbance. He was given a large room in a high part of a building used as a livery stable.

The odors from below were almost unbearable, but Pancho was allowed enough contacts to order some better furniture purchased, at his own expense, and brought in. He cleaned the place thoroughly, too. He exercised all the personal charm at his command, keeping the turnkeys and jail crew entranced. He *was* known to them, no matter what the high-ups had hoped; Pancho Villa was a name in all of Mexico. And here he was, a fine fellow, genial, generous, kind. He sensed this reaction to him. Compared to his former cells, this room offered the life of a potentate. In time, friends and other visitors—the curious, the eager ones anxious to wish him well—were allowed to visit him. Best of all, he struck up a friendship with another prisoner who was educated. They talked often, and at length.

"You know much that I do not," Pancho complimented him. "How you know so many things, eh?"

The new friend, a younger man, was surprised. "It's just that I like to read. Don't you?"

Pancho smiled sadly. "Read? Me, my friend? I have not had time to learn. Nor opportunity. Who teaches a peon horse wrangler to read? His mother? Who teaches her? His father? He was long dead. Nobody taught Pancho Villa."

The younger man was touched. "You can't—sir, you mean you can't even read, or write either, maybe? Pancho Villa, the great liberator? General Villa?"

Pancho smiled again, shaking his head. "You teach me, eh? We ·have not much to do here." He was speaking softly, wistfully. "I will buy us the books? I can do that. I'll be very grateful, if you will teach me some things."*

The young teacher was not long with Pancho, but he was there long enough to open that most revealing of all doors, the printed word. Pancho was enthralled. With nothing to do all day but practice, he learned fast. He never developed what could be called a classical vocabulary, but he did learn "newspaper Spanish" in both printing and hand script. He would work with pen and ink for hours, absorbed. He admitted that he was fascinated by the stylized writing in Mexico, which included many fine flourishes or purely ornamental curlicues. Most of all he was impressed by

————

*It is regrettable that the young teacher's name is not recorded. Pancho himself could not remember it in later years.

the newly acquired ability to write his own signature. For the remainder of his life he was likely to *make* occasion to sign things, with considerable ceremony. This, he understood vaguely, gratified some inner feeling, gave him stature in his own mind. (Thus, it was that his signature which should have been a rare collector's item 40 years or so after his death, actually was very common. Not that it wasn't appreciated. It was; it was to be found in the homes, offices, and libraries of many a family, carefully preserved. Perhaps by the year 2,000 enough copies will have disappeared to make the remaining ones valuable.)

Here is the way in which the Chihuahuan centaur, the Tiger of the North, the Great Insurrecto, the Peon Liberator, signed his name:

In a short while Pancho purchased a typewriter. He received it with glee, knowing, but not caring, that he was like a child with a new toy. He spent long hours with it that first week. He had been granted counsel by now, and his attorney was helpful in many personal as well as legal things. He would order the lawyer to bring paper and practice sheets; would tap out letters, poems, words of songs, anything he could contrive.

One of the courtrooms was in the same building that housed Pancho. A cell in which prisoners would be placed to testify at court was separated from judge, jury, and spectators by an iron grating. Persuasive Pancho inveigled permission to come into that cell, and from here he could visit with officials if court was not in session. He saw them learn to welcome his visits. He knew that he could be good company any time; with his background, his record, he could easily fascinate them, and doing so gave him pleasure.

Among the court attaches thus impressed was yet another young man, one who soon responded to Pancho's spirit with a feeling of kinship. His name was Carlos Juaregui, and he was a clerk. One day Pancho entered that adjoining cell, saw young Carlos in the court room alone, and spoke to him.

"I'm inquiring about my case," Pancho said.

He meant, actually, his typewriter case; the lawyer had taken

123

it out with the machine, having borrowed it, but returned the machine alone. Young Carlos thought Pancho meant his personal court case, and replied on that basis. Coming close to the grating, he said in a low voice, "General, your case is going from bad to worse. They are framing you more every week. They'll never release you. So why don't you escape? It's your only chance, sir!"

Pancho, surprised, went to the grating, close to the lad. "Escape?"

"Yes sir. It would be easy. You could do it. I am ready to help you. If necessary, I'll even go with you."

What more could a prisoner ask? And yet—Pancho couldn't trust anybody, he reflected. He had been repeatedly betrayed. Promises, after being accepted, had backfired on him; too many treacheries against him were remembered now. But as the young man said, he had no chance here, he had nothing to lose by trying. Carlos seemed to be very sincere. Pancho agreed to think the matter over and decide soon.

Next day Carlos asked if he was ready and Pancho said yes.

"I'll file through one of the bars of the grating," the younger man whispered eagerly. "Then we will be able to walk right out of the courthouse. I give you my word, General, I'll take you out to the street without any risk."

"Not so fast. First, go bring me two pistols, one hundred cartridges, and some clothing. I have the money for it. Get clothing such as a lawyer might wear."

"Good idea, sir."

The items were smuggled in to him that same week. It wasn't hard to do, really. Much of the time the courtroom was not in use, although the clerk had normal reason to be there often and so his presence excited no suspicion. He had been careful not to be seen talking with General Villa, his hero.

Pancho had long since grown a heavy mustache, and the pictures taken and published of him to date showed him wearing it. Hair was thick and bushy over his ears. Also, he had rarely been seen for two years or so in any clothing other than his charro costume. In his cell now, therefore, he made plans to change his appearance when the time came. He had been allowed a razor. Scissors were brought in.

Filing through the iron grating took more time than either man had anticipated. For one thing, the cut was low down, about knee high, so as not to be readily seen. Also, the file made a screeching noise that seemed to penetrate all through the building, and Pancho was fearful. After the first attempt a janitor peered curiously into the courtroom and asked about the sound.

"I was repairing a desk," answered Carlos Juaregui, smiling. "A screw has come through a panel to make a drawer stick."

The janitor went on, satisfied. While Pancho nervously paced and worried, Carlos waited until covering outside sounds were made. He would file rapidly if a team of horses or a troop of cavalry went by with hoofs clattering on the pavement. Then he might have to wait two days for another chance. One Sunday, though, a municipal band came to the courthouse and began a concert just outside the windows of Pancho's cell. Simultaneously Carlos slipped into the court room and began a fast filing.

"How did the band happen to be here, my friend?" Pancho wondered. "How fortunate it came!"

"The judge issued an order for it. I am the clerk, so I wrote the order for him; a special invitation. The judge doesn't know about it yet, but maybe he will."

Both laughed, and Pancho embraced his friend through the bars. Their conspiracy was now nearing its climax and he felt exhilarated. The heavy bar of hardened steel was cut almost through. "Will you be ready, sir?" Carlos asked, keeping a wary eye on the doors.

"I'm ready now," Pancho spoke eagerly. "Cut the bar at once. I have great strength, I can pull it aside and spread the others apart to squeeze through. Then if we move that high-backed chair in front of the hole, nobody will suspect anything for a while. Is the file cutting fast?"

"Half an hour more, maybe."

He worked hard, and Pancho in the gloom of his cell worked, too.

Thus at about 4:30 in the afternoon, following the siesta hour so that the city was stirring again, the court clerk Carlos Juaregui might have been seen walking casually out of the building in company with what obviously was an attorney-at-law.

The attorney wore a gray business suit, an overcoat, a derby hat, and dark eye glasses. Under one arm was the *licenciado's* inevitable badge of office, a leather brief case—though what Pancho hoped the passerby would never suspect was that this case contained not legal papers, but a .45 revolver and a lot of cartridges tied in a scarf. A second pistol was concealed under the lawyer's belt. He evidently was suffering some from a cold, too, for his free hand kept a handkerchief to his nose, and he blew it or appeared to sneeze every few yards, even as he tried to converse with Juaregui. The lawyer obviously was not an outdoorsy sort, probably did no horseback riding, gardening, or any such, but worked constantly indoors; his skin was not tanned, it was pallid. He wore short hair, had no mustache, and was definitely stooped as if from endless work at a desk. Thus he flowed into the city's sidewalk traffic, attracting no attention whatsoever.

They moved rather slowly (Juaregui twice had to restrain the general from hurrying, so eager was Pancho to be away), and came to an automobile parked beside the Santiago Custom House, near the prison. Casually, they climbed into it and drove away.

Behind him in his cell, Pancho had left a form made of clothing and blankets in his prison bunk. He had studied the prison turnkey's routine. That rather stupid menial, he knew, would peek on Sunday night and again on Monday at breakfast, think that he saw a man sleeping or maybe sulking in his bunk. When the man hadn't stirred by Monday noon, hadn't eaten for twenty-four hours, Pancho knew there'd be an investigation.

The thought of it set him laughing here in the car with his friend Carlos; that and the heady air of freedom. He inhaled deeply, threw out his chest, smacked his lips. The Tiger of the North was preparing to roar again.

14

PANCHO quickly realized that he must not laugh loudly on the streets, must do nothing to attract attention. This wasn't easy, but he forced self-control even while impatience rode with him. The escape car had been hired beforehand, and he with his invaluable young friend Carlos Juaregui drove in it to Toluca as prearranged. They could not know how soon the alarm for Pancho would be sounded, but they agreed it was best to take no chances, so they stayed as inconspicuous as possible.

On the streets of Toluca they repeatedly caught people staring at Pancho—or did they? Perhaps it was imagination, Pancho murmured. As they turned a corner a well-dressed man caught his eye, smiled broadly and suddenly stepped in front of him. Pancho almost drew a pistol and shot the man before he could speak.

"A ticket in the lottery, *señores?*" the salesman whined, ingratiatingly. "For two pesos you may be rich. Only two pesos for half a million that will enable you—"

They pushed the peddler aside and hurried on. A few minutes later a barefoot, humpbacked crone blocked his path with her shapeless body clad in rags. She was holding up an incongruously beautiful gardenia, fragrant and fresh as April. Pancho the "attorney-at-law" shifted his brief case long enough to get a coin from his pocket and give it to her. He took the flower, a thing of perfection, and pinned it not on his lapel, but on the shoulder of her miserable dress, then hastened away.

She turned to stare at them, spellbound. Her toothless mouth was open, her hand like a claw clutching the coin. He knew she couldn't recognize him, that she probably couldn't even see him clearly through her rheumy eyes, but she was muttering a blessing. The act had pleased him immensely; she was plainly one of the downtrodden peons.

Together the two men walked to the railroad station at Palmillas and took a train for Crucero Gonzales. Thence they fled to Guadalajara and on through Colima to Manzanillo on the coast. Juaregui paused long enough to get some "different" clothing for himself, then purchased passage for two on the SS *Ramon Corral* for Mazatlan. Pancho made them stay in hiding here for a time, making cautious inquiry to see if any alarm had been sounded for the escapee, Villa.

It had been sounded indeed, he soon learned. Telegraph wires were hot with the news. People everywhere were talking. That Pancho—ha! He is the slick one, *no es verdad, amigo?* No prison can hold him, eh? They had him down there in the capital to kill him. It was Huerta's doing, not Madero's. Huerta ought to be the one hanged, not Pancho the peons' friend. I wonder where he ran to? If they saw him they shot him down, we can be sure. The dirty bastards, it's the way they do; they *say* he tried to escape, as an excuse for shooting him. I'll bet he is dead and they are just saying that he ran away. But maybe not; no, it is hard to kill Pancho, for he had a special saint to guard him, and he has our prayers. Viva Pancho. Viva Villa. Long may he live, wherever he is.

It was good to hear such reactions; he choked with emotion. Travelling incognito, the two fugitives hastened on, this time to Guaymas, pushing northward all the time, getting farther and farther from Mexico City. Pancho longed for his hideout in the Sierra Gamon. He thought once to bid Juaregui goodbye and strike out on his own, but such a plan presented too many difficulties.

"You do not know if your men could be contacted, General," Carlos reminded him. "They would assemble again, yes. But you could be rearrested before word could be passed around, for you would not have enough men with you to protect you against Huerta's soldiers. He'd grab you if he could, probably shoot you down at once."

It was true, and Pancho recognized it. He couldn't count on any reprieve from President Madero if caught again now. His first imperative move was to find safety, then contact Madero himself. He had been imprisoned four months right under Madero's nose and the president had not been able to release him. Pancho had to know where he stood.

From Guaymas, therefore, he made cloak-and-dagger exit once more, fleeing by night in a "borrowed" automobile. This vehicle, a touring car of already ancient vintage, was one of the few that had found their way to the resort town. He himself knew nothing about operating it, and Juaregui knew less, but a pistol stuck in the owner's belly solved the problem. They bumped and bounced over the poor roadway until, some forty kilometers out, an axle broke. Here they bade their chauffeur goodbye with a coin and a warning, walked several miles, "borrowed" saddle horses, and eventually showed up at the Sonora-Arizona international border. Pancho knew they might have found hospice in Nogales, the town that straddles the line like a cowboy forking a horse, but he also knew it was guarded by U.S. Immigration officers who could be nosey. Even if he and Carlos slipped into town, the *gringo* officers might detect them on the American side and start deportation proceedings. So the two went on to the larger city of Tucson, Arizona. First thing Pancho did there was to visit the telegraph office and send this message:

HIS EXCELLENCY FRANCISCO MADERO
PRESIDENT REPUBLICA DE MEXICO
CIUDAD MEXICO, D.F.

FELICITATIONS AND PRAYERS FOR YOUR CON-
TINUED SUCCESS AS THE CHAMPION OF OUR PEO-
PLES FREEDOM STOP MY SERVICES AGAIN ARE
YOURS TO COMMAND
FRANCISCO VILLA

It was the door to the telegraph office which interrupted his thinking and brought up sharply the realization that he hadn't made love to any girl for months. As he would have left the office, an American woman entering let the door slam. It struck Pancho, forehead and belt. No harm was done, yet the woman was instantly contrite for her carelessness.

"Oh I'm *so* sorry!" she apologized at once. "It was all my fault, bursting in this way. Please forgive me."

Unconsciously perhaps, she reached to place a hand on Pancho's arm, pleading, her wide eyes looking into his eyes. She was not strikingly beautiful, but she was young in years and Pancho saw that she was dressed in a way that hinted at much of interest underneath. In the quick moment there, her touch was electrifying.

He stepped back, bowed low and murmured, "*Por nada seño-rita.*" Then remembering she was American, added, "It was nothing."

That should normally have ended the trivial incident, but always there was something arresting about Pancho Villa, and he well knew it. If he looked straight at another person, that one seldom could just walk away, couldn't end the interview but had to wait his pleasure, so hypnotic was his personality. He never understood this, but he liked it, and used it freely. They continued talking and soon had introduced themselves, though caution made him use a fictitious name. Thus while the astonished clerk Carlos Juaregui waited none too patiently, his friend General Villa made a date with an American girl.

They had dinner early, at 6 p.m. No girl ever had a more

129

enthusiastic host, nor a more romantic one. He had bought some new clothing, another charro costume that set off his fine figure. She revealed that she was a widow, and a tourist in Arizona for the first time. He rented a surrey and drove her onto the desert. There was a lap robe, and it with the seat cushion served them very well.

When he brought her back to her hotel toward midnight, she was already experiencing a bit of after-panic, he observed wryly.

"But you *must* marry me!" she protested, there by the carriage. "I'll be sure to have a baby. Whatever can I do?"

He shrugged. "Many ladies have babies. Many have *my* babies, señora, and are proud. Is good, eh, what we do? You like?"

She was sobbing and did not answer.

"You go to your room now. You sleep. Tomorrow you feel fine. Maybe you not have baby. Maybe you do. If you do—" he shrugged expressively again, "is fine anyway. Maybe he look joos' like me, eh? You be proud!"

With that he kissed her forehead, turned her toward the door, and drove away. He never saw the young woman again, nor heard if she did or didn't bear his child. Life had too many interests, new demands every waking moment, to dwell long on one night's pleasure. But he felt that meeting her had been a fortunate encounter, supplying a need.

Pancho soon found that many forces in Mexico were working against Madero, hence indirectly against him. He focused on only one treachery—Huerta's. He knew now from hard personal experience that Huerta was a criminal of the worst type who would try, as Orozco had tried, to overthrow Madero.

From Tucson he contacted General José Maria Maytorena, Governor of the Mexican State of Sonora, and confirmed Huerta's treason. Maytorena then sent Pancho one thousand pesos. The money was a godsend; most of the gold that he had been permitted to carry with him to the Mexico City prison had been spent. With this help Pancho was able to buy five horses, saddles, and bridles, also guns and ammunition. With great care, he rounded up four Mexican nationals who were loyal to Madero and spent more than two weeks teaching them to shoot fast and straight, to ride like inspired hellions, leaning low in their saddles and swinging their sabres. Cactus plants in one Tucson area were cut to shreds by imaginary cavalry charges of the five men, especially the cholla or "jumping" cactus because it grew to about the height of an infantryman and because its vicious fish-hook spines would exact toll for carelessness. He led his men in teaching the horses to jump, not as show horses in a ring would, but as excited, battle-stimulated mounts might do. These four men and mounts thus were prepared to drill any new recruits.

Then on a night in March of 1913, Pancho told his beloved young friend Carlos Juaregui goodbye, promising to meet him again in Mexico City. (Carlos was to say that Pancho had kidnapped him at pistol point after escaping prison.) They shook hands and embraced one another in true affection. Without further ado, Pancho Villa—*General* Villa again now—mounted his new horse, signalled to his four happy henchmen, and headed back south. They crossed the border in the dark of the moon at a point near Las Partidas; a general, with an army of four, riding once more to change the course of empire. It could have been pitiful—except that the general was, indeed, Pancho Villa. That was magic enough.

He soon discovered that his old followers were happy to answer his new call, bringing their friends. Within a few weeks the four had multiplied to more than four hundred. All were men who held a fanatical loyalty for Villa and who knew the wilderness of Sonora and Chihuahua well. They were ideally suited for guerrilla fighting, that most adventurous, exciting warfare of all. Pancho worked hard at their training. They were not adequately equipped or armed because each had come with whatever he could gather. In appearance his men again were a ragtag bandit band. Many were barefoot. Most had on overalls or some unbleached homespun garments of nondescript cut, barely adequate to cover. Virtually all had the great straw sombrero. Few of them ever shaved because there were few razors, hence beards gave them a ferocious aspect in which they took delight. It was sport to practice scowling, grimacing, snarling, and screaming at one another as they leaned over saddle horns in a wild cavalry charge. This very rehearsal, this preconceived technique of terror, Pancho felt, might stand them in good stead later; often ten men of frightening mien and manner can rout one hundred trained only for orderly firing.

So, here was the Tiger of the North baring his fangs again, a happy friend told him. He resumed stalking his prey in much the manner he had begun it some years before—by moving on strongholds of rich ranchers. Among the first of these was, of all things, another unit of the fabulous Don Luis Terrazas empire, the Carmen hacienda. It had not been touched before, but now the Villistas rode up to it with typical fanfare. They were welcomed as Villa always was, with much waving of banners and shouting of "Viva!" Viva Villa; long live Villa. It was the same significant cry. He felt it strengthen his spirit.

First thing the welcoming peons did was show Pancho the tree where they were tied to be whipped by the administrator of the Carmen farms.

"And where is the administrator, my friends?" demanded Pancho.

"He has gone inside," they pointed grinning. "He saw your horses and was afraid."

"Ha! A smart man. *Luis!*"

A husky young corporal spurred close to the general and saluted.

"We need the farm administrator, Luis. Take maybe four men, eh? Whatever you think you need. There may be shooting. Luis, practice your pistol draw. Now. Watch me—GO!"

Both men's hands were flashes of lightning; almost instantaneously each stared at the muzzle of the other's gun.

"*Bueno*, Luis! You might have killed me, for a fact. Now see to it you keep alert. I am proud of you; I want to stay proud. And you want to stay alive, *no es verdad?*

"*Si*, my general." The worshipful young warrior saluted again and hastened away.

The waiting was not long but it gave him time to study the people here, the workers. All were poorly clad, half starved, miserably housed. It was the same old story, Pancho saw with renewed bitterness. When the guilty man was brought, terror shone in his eyes, and for good cause.

Pancho took him by the arm in an almost comradely fashion and led him into the throng of peons that had gathered, nearly a hundred of them now. One barefoot man stood with a shoulder sagging lower than the other. He removed his hat as Pancho approached, as most did, and looked up with an expression akin to reverence.

"You are crippled?" Pancho asked.

132

The man nodded. "A broken shoulder, General."

"*He* broke it?"

Several spoke up at once, telling the horror of that incident, of how the administrator had used a heavy hickory singletree to strike the worker, missing his head—where such a blow would surely have killed him—and hitting the shoulder. Others now bared their own wounds, some healed, some still raw. Pancho heard them speak of persons beaten until they crawled off and died, for no offense except trying to run away. It was the administrator's custom to tie the victims' hands tightly, pull the rope over a tree limb and stretch the arms for half an hour before the whippings began. "Here is the very tree, General," the people pointed again. "That is the limb. See, the rope marks show. Only yesterday one of us was so punished." Pancho nodded and turned back to the guilty one.

"Your keys, *señor*," he demanded, quietly. "To the warehouses, the commissaries, all the supplies."

They were surrendered at once and tossed to some peon men who gleefully ran to start the looting.

"Now *señor*, is the time for some entertainment. There is a smooth wall; there, that building. It is plastered neatly. You will go stand with your back to it."

"Do not kill me, General Villa!" He dropped to his knees. "I beg of you in the name of the Vir—"

"*Go stand against the wall!*"

The man went there, trembling.

"Now, because you liked to stretch arms before whipping, you must stretch yours. High!"

"But *señor!* General Villa!"

"High! Wide apart . . . like that. Open your hands with their backs flat against the wall. Spread your fingers. Back, flat. And I warn you, do not move!"

The hapless one froze against the wall. Pancho stood some forty feet from him, still very calm. He glanced around once. Not a sound could be heard. Eyes of the men spectators were wide; mouths hung open. Some of the women had pulled their black shawls over their faces; several crossed themselves and lips were moving in prayer. Pancho turned slowly back to the man who, surely, must have been dying by degrees from sheer terror.

The famous Villa mustache had grown back, and Pancho

reached now to groom it with the knuckle of his forefinger. He parted it meditatively, pushing its two wings aside, lifting the delicately pointed ends. It was not a "dandy" mustache, not the meticulously waxed type that is too neat and pretty; it was heavier, more masculine. He knew that it did truly add an illusion of strength to an already strong man; that it gave him years, lifted him into the forties. He was not vain about it—at least no more vain than any man with a mustache is likely to be. It was just that it had value, so he said years later, as an identification piece. People had come to expect the big mustache on Pancho Villa, as they had come to expect the unexpected in his actions.

They got the unexpected now. After a seeming eternity of meditation he suddenly whirled. As if by magic again the two revolvers were in his hands, and spurting flame.

They did not fire simultaneously, but alternately, and with aim, from eye level. The speed was not fast, perhaps a little faster than the ticking of a grandfather clock, the shots a little less than one second apart. Six from the left-hand gun, six from the right.

When they were empty he lowered them, holstered one and calmly began re-loading the other, blowing out the barrel, admiring the weapon in his hand.

At the wall, the man apparently had been pinned to it like a bear skin stretched for drying. He did not drop, did not move. His eyes were huge, open, horrified and unbelieving. Blood? There was no blood. At least none flowed, none dripped from his white shirt or his head to form the usual pool in the hard-packed soil.

Then as the seconds ticked by the people saw what Pancho had done. The spread fingers had been his target. Yet his bullets had touched no flesh. Accurately spaced about two inches apart, beginning outside the thumbs and going between each finger, they had formed a perfect arc through the fan-shaped hands. Their holes were neatly drilled in the wall, although before sundown each leaden slug was dug out and pocketed as a souvenir, Pancho learned. The nerve-shattered victim fell on his face. It is doubtful if he ever was normal again.

Forever after, General Villa discovered himself tagged with one more in the list of his affectionate or at least respectful nicknames—Pancho Pistolas.

His next major move was on March 19, 1913, when he led the Villistas riding hell-for-leather against the town of Satevo. It was spectacular action again, with the shouting and the shooting and the screaming and the blood. The name of Villa was fast rebuilding. It had never actually lost strength, he discovered happily, but it was gaining more. He realized that the gain was due in large measure to his penchant for making each drama personal. He could inject himself into the limelight with unerring instinct, partly because he loved it and partly because he knew that power could be built on individual fame.

After the easy conquest of Satevo, for example, he dismounted to shake hands in the cheering crowd. He would pat this citizen on a shoulder, squeeze that one's arm, hug this very old lady, or embrace some fat matron with a child on her hip. The adulation for him knew no bounds, he noted; he was a people's hero at every turn.

Among those who crowded up to him was a young girl carrying a baby in her arms. She was perhaps seventeen and so sexually ripe that her every feature and motion proclaimed it, though in her great brown eyes was now a monumental confusion akin to fear. The babe was a miniature of its mother in its instantaneous appeal. Pancho broke into a smile that was like a sunny day dawning, reached out to take the little one from her arms. Then he caught himself up short.

"Ho, *madrecita*," he spoke gently. "Why are tears in your eyes? Why do you come to Pancho Villa crying? Is the baby ill?"

"No General. He is well. But we will both starve if a lie cannot be corrected. General Villa, the priest here is telling everybody that my baby is your son!"

"No! I have never seen you before! I have never been here. How can he say such a thing?"

People had gathered close, enthralled. Pancho's anger was as impressive as his generosity could be. The girl glanced at her neighbors before she reluctantly spoke, and she lowered her head as she did so.

"The baby's father is the priest himself," she murmured.

Pancho sent for the man. He was a virile young padre, who could not, perhaps, have been expected to be perfect.

"Not even the most ferocious animal in the wilderness refuses

135

to take care of its children," Pancho spoke directly, as always. "Priest or devil, Father, you shall die promptly at my own hands if you do not publicly admit that the child here is your son, and swear to make yourself responsible for his support and care."

The priest knelt and made public confession. "It is true," cried he, from the depths of guilt. "Shoot me anyway, for I deserve it."

He was not punished; at least not by man. But within a few weeks he died of fever, Pancho learned.

The incidents, the dramatic scenes, the episodes, in the new and swift rise to power, came almost hourly, he found. Things "happened" to Pancho Villa, wherever he was. Boredom was utterly unknown to him; if no excitement awaited his arrival, he invariably generated some.

"In all his adult life it is doubtful if Francisco Villa has ever spent appreciable time just doing nothing," one American newspaper reporter wrote in a feature story for his editor. "He is never seen loafing, never relaxed. The *mañana* Mexican who is cartooned lolling against a sunny wall with his *sombrero* over his face? Not this Pancho Pistolas, this Chihuahuan centaur, this Tiger of the North! He is vibrant. He is driven. He gets things done. No more exciting individual has ever lived."

It was a good summation, and when he was shown a copy of it Pancho was pleased. He read it aloud, in English, slowly, proud not only of its content but of the fact that he could read at all. The months in prison had given him valuable time to think, he realized now; miserable as it was, the place had also helped correct his main deficiency.

"Me, I am now educate," he told the newspaper reporter. He tapped his own extended chest proudly. "I learn to reads, eh? And write on the tapwriter, *seguro si*. Me. Pancho!" It was still an incredible achievement, even to him.

"That's mighty fine, General. Uh—what all did you write?"

"Ever' damn theeng. Words. Sen—sentences? *Si*, sentences— ¿Sabe usted?—the many words, in the chain. You onderstan'? Lak you writes, eh?"

The reporter smiled fondly, nodding in comradeship. "One of us! Tell you what, Pancho. You chuck all this and I'll get you a job as a star reporter. How about that?"

Pancho considered, frowning. "St-star?" The *gringo* word was familiar to him in its literal sense. "*La estrella?* For why I make the report about heem, eh? What the star do?" He looked to heaven. And he wasn't joking.

Again the American smiled. "It's just a term we use. Forget it. But I'm glad you learned how to read. Books, huh? Magazines? Papers?"

Pancho nodded; he truly could read many simple things now, even some printed in English, and was forever delighted with that achievement. He considered himself genuinely educated.

His penchant for dramatic scenes brought him personal pleasure. Moreover, he observed that it was contagious to a degree, and he encouraged this because he knew it was valuable as a builder of efficiency and morale.

"You must learn to fight like *me*," he would say to his recruits. "Men who follow Pancho Villa are not sheep crouching in a trench to fire now and then over the sand bags. They are tigers who spring off a cliff onto their enemies and chew them to pieces. *¿Sabe usted?*

He saw that they did understand, and that they liked it. "The tiger-type fighting may not be as efficient as the West Point style," the same reporter wrote later, "but it is a whale of a lot more fun, and if you get your hide punctured, so be it. The typical Villista would grin and shrug at any mention of the fact that his life was exceedingly dangerous. What good is life if it is dull? Better to live six years with Villa than sixty as a slave."

Pancho liked that so well he gave the reporter a private car and chauffeur. He had that last sentence translated into Spanish, printed on little cards and given away by the thousands. "Me, I make the—how you say him, *amigo?*—the prop—the popper—the prop—" He grimaced and gave up. He never could say the word *propaganda*.

Pancho, feeling educated at last, now told himself that he could no longer be content with mere loyalty and enthusiasm from his men. He was attracting more and more recruits, but he sensed as never before that they came with varying talents and capacities. A low economic level begets low mentality, men with money are more intelligent, he felt. Most of his soldiers came from economic zero, and inasmuch as he had grandiose new plans, he needed a better type, at least for those immediately around him. So, in this year of 1913 he conceived the idea of forming a very *special* cavalry troop.

These men, carefully picked, trained to razor-edge sharpness, indoctrinated with courage such as few warriors ever know, would be his favored fighters, he told reporter friends. They would be the banner bearers. They would be the sudden and irresistible attackers that turned the tide in battle, the reliable ones to call on in any emergency need. They would be completely trustworthy down to the last man. They would be able to think and fight and take charge and accomplish things as if they were controlled by Pancho Villa's own brain. So he told the reporters, somewhat oratorically, while striding back and forth before them in his headquarters tent one evening. He saw that they were dubious, and this made him even more determined.

He personally began to pick men for that troop. In a sense *all* Villistas were his personal choosing, but these were the ones who had risen to the top. He conceived unique tests for them. He demanded impossible stunts of endurance and skill.

"There is of course nothing new about this ambition," one reporter wrote. "Rulers in every land since history began seem to have created such a close-knit group of aides or protectors. Even the Vatican itself, which needs them least of all, is made picturesque not so much by His Holiness as by his Swiss Guard. Caesar had them, Nero had them, Napoleon had them. Perhaps they give any leader an illusion of greater personal strength— though it is less illusion than reality. For these men, these close ones, can carry on when the leader himself must sleep or seek recreation. They can back him up when there is any unexpected need."

Again Pancho read the summation and was pleased. It had expressed what he himself felt about it but had been unable to put sharply into words. He was particularly glad to be classed with Napoleon, for he had read a few bits about that conqueror.

"Be damn!" he exclaimed, putting the paper down. "I am esmart, eh? Me, I am educate now, I don' make the so many damn fool meestake. Is good. You write the good truth, *amigo del periodico*. Some day I make you reech. You lak him?" He smiled archly.

"I like him," nodded the reporter, fondly. "But right now let's just get on with the war."

Pancho picked out two hundred very special men, then he gave them everything. He showered them with praise and demanded much, he equipped them with know-how and material. He soon came to love them so much that he wanted a fitting name for them.

He was in the town of Ascencion, Chihuahua, when he found that name. Late one afternoon the picked men were wheeling their horses in drills on a flat mountain country mesa. The sun burst with color as only a Mexican sun can do. Reds, purples, magentas, greens, yellows, every tint and hue splashed onto the cliffs and pinnacles, flowed down the slopes and filled the canyons, spilled into the valleys and plains. Some of the rays caught the prized cavalrymen just right, from where General Villa was watching. They had moved to a rise in the land and so were above him, and thus were silhouetted against a turquoise eastern sky.

"Look!" cried Pancho, elated, to officers at his side. "The sun has turned them to gold! My Dorados! My Golden Ones!"

The name held, and with it they rode into the pages of Mexican history.

15

HE NEVER quite understood his own powers, nor really ever tried to analyze them, but by Spring of 1913 Francisco Villa knew that he had risen high again and was ready for action.

He had attracted more and more capable associates, including several Americans. One of the latter was a kindred spirit named Charles A. Ward. Pancho learned that Charlie had been a brash kid in Seattle, then a sailor, an Arctic dog team driver, an Alaskan gold panner. Now he had slid down continent to join "the Mexican Revolution."

Pancho eyed him much as a big brother would have, fondly but severely. "W'at you do here, yo'ng man. Maybe I keel you, eh?"

"You are a big bag of wind . . . sir!"

The big bag of wind glared.

"Beeg bag of weend? You call *me* that? I be doggone damn!"

"Sir, where I come from even the children cuss better than that. Maybe I stick around and teach you English."

Pancho burst into laughter much like a burro's braying.

"*Si*, you estick aroun'. I make you *mucho hombre*."

Charlie Ward stuck around, learned much, returned to America, and became a national figure as president of Brown and Bigelow in St. Paul and as a philanthropist. Pancho loved him like a brother. Immediately he put Charlie to work as mechanical engineer, and the young adventurer rewarded him by developing Mexico's first armored automobiles. He even made spare steel wheels with flanges, so the cars could be used on train tracks. Pancho counted him a genius.

By such unerring instincts, General Villa by May of 1913 had developed another dangerous military force. On May 29 he led it in an attack on the city of Saucillo, capturing it with ease. Raids on lesser towns followed, until August 25 when he roared into San Andres and took it too. He distributed the loot among the populace as was his custom; soon he was a god on a pedestal again, and knew it. The knowledge always lifted his spirits.

Meanwhile he discovered that another name had loomed on the Mexican horizon. Venustiana Carranza, Governor of the State of Coahuila, had come out against Huerta and elected himself as the first leader of the Constitutional revolution. Huerta's troops had defeated him, so he retreated into Sonora. There Carranza contacted Pancho Villa and asked his support.

Villa promised it on one condition—that he have complete freedom of action, be allowed to command his own troops without interference from any one. Thus once again the bold centaur was "commanding the commander."

Carranza accepted Pancho's independence gracefully. He even sent new groups to join him under such leaders as Calixto Contreras and Tomas Urbina. These combined forces later were to be known as the Northern Division. Immediately they made sporadic raids on such Huerta units as they could find. This included capture of the city of Parral. Then, on November 5, 1913, Pancho led them against the bigger Chihuahua City.

Chihuahua City was well defended by Generals Orozco, Caraveo, Salazar, and Rojas, with strong fortifications, and Pancho knew it. He, therefore, made frontal attack, pretended to retreat in order to draw out the defenders, then did a quick about-face and counterattacked. Days passed with this sort of bloody maneu-vering, enough to establish the fact in all the newspapers and enemy spies that Villa and his men were there. This was precisely what he wanted. He smiled constantly, feeling happy and high.

On November 13, he appeared to call the battle a draw and retire. Conspicuously he sent all of his *trains* southward, but the cream of his fighting force lay hidden behind the rocks. Then at night these men quietly filed out in the opposite direction. He had timed the maneuver with care. Safely out of range of Chihua-hua city, the Villistas came onto a charcoal train rolling south-ward from Ciudad Juarez.

In the strange course of events, Juarez had fallen into enemy hands again, but Pancho still counted it the headquarters town of a man he hated, Don Luis Terrazas, most arrogant of the rich ranchers. He had carefully plotted to oust the Terrazas forces a second time, and this charcoal train was part of the planning.

He stopped the train easily with the old trick of grease on the tracks of an uphill pull. He sprang to the caboose and burst the door open, led half a dozen of his men inside. The conductor, two brakemen, and an important fourth man stared in open-mouthed astonishment.

"Greetings, *amigos*," said the leader, smiling broadly. "You have company. I am Pancho Villa, at your service. It is necessary that we send a message back to Juarez. *Señor*, the telegraph set." Pancho had known an operator would be aboard; all trains, sub-ject to military use now, carried operators for either the telegraph or the newer wireless. "And do not make any mistakes. My Sergeant Benavides here knows the code well, *sabe usted?*"

The fourth man in the caboose did truly understand. He saw the Villistas' rifles, their twin pistols, their knives, and their battle-hardened expressions. A message was ticked off to the dispatcher: CANNOT PROCEED BECAUSE RAILS DESTROYED BY VILLA FORCES. PLEASE WIRE INSTRUCTIONS.

It was signed by the train conductor, who presently received orders to return to Juarez.

Pancho was delighted. This was precisely what he wanted, what he had planned. He had verified his presence near Chihuahua City far to the south of Juarez. Meanwhile 2000 of his armed men had already boarded the charcoal train and were emptying the cars. This took a while, and every soldier was blacked by the dust, Pancho noted. He made a joke of it, and his men accepted it in good spirits. It was not a long run back to Juarez, yet there was time for sleep and the tired Villa soldiers were not fastidious.

The train stopped at each little station. A few soldiers would go in almost casually and capture the telegraph operator, then wire ahead that the train was making safe progress back to Juarez and all was well. The townspeople in these outlying communities all were asleep, and could hardly have been suspicious even if they had been awake. Pancho himself was in the caboose. He sprawled on one of the bunks there and snored so loudly the guards could scarcely hear the clicking of the wheels. He had already given his orders, his subordinates knew exactly what to do. About twenty minutes out of Juarez an orderly touched his shoulder, shook him.

"General . . . General Villa, sir, it is time."

He sat up at once, rubbing a huge hand through his hair and grinning at his men in greeting. He looked out the dirty window over his bunk. The night was black. He looked at his watch— well past midnight. He stretched his great bear-like arms wide, yawned prodigiously, and stood up.

"We have some fun, eh my friends?" said he, buckling on his pistol belts. "But no shooting this time. It is too late at night to shoot; would wake up all the girls, eh?" They laughed with him.

Having faked perfectly the succession of messages about the returning train, Pancho's army thus rode unquestioned right into the heart of Juarez. A squad of his men crouched with cocked rifles in the engine and tender. The uninteresting cars of "charcoal" attracted no attention whatsoever because no sign of human life showed on them. The required clanging and whistling and huffing and puffing all seemed a part of routine.

Once the train stopped at the station, though, it suddenly came alive with its 2000 armed men. They made almost no noise. No shouting this time, no talking, not even a whisper, just the muffled sounds of jumping to the ground, with here and there a quiet click of metal, as three lines quickly formed. No orders were given, or needed. The columns, led by officers whom Pancho had carefully briefed, filed off to the city's three army camps. Even at these camps no suspicions were aroused as the contingents approached.

"Captain Contreras," a leader would say, "with a company returning from patrol."

"Advance and give the password."

It was enough. Before the sleepy guards realized it, each such "advance" had overwhelmed and captured them. Still unrecognized, the Vilistas marched right on down the tent streets, deployed effectively and waited with cocked rifles while their officers called at the enemy commanders' tents. No defender guessed that Pancho Villa was anywhere within range of Juarez. *These* attackers were not Villistas, not even men; they were obviously sons of Satan direct from hell itself. Even the faces were as black as night, their eyes shining through, their grinning teeth like the fangs of fiends. Villa's men had made good use of the charcoal dust. Only a few of the Juarez defenders escaped. The rest were shot or made prisoners. General Villa ordered that no prisoners be killed.

The next morning Pancho was in a luxurious Juarez bathtub— one of the few he had ever enjoyed—and he was making wash-up sounds like a man strangling an octopus. Suddenly his aide Luis rapped sharply on the bathroom door.

"General Villa, trains are coming from Chihuahua City! They are loaded with troops, sir, to drive us from Juarez!"

The door burst open. Two maids had been at work cleaning the bedroom. They froze in their tracks, not at the news, at which they would have been insensitive, but at the spectacle of Pancho Villa, the Tiger of the North, standing stark naked and wet before them, glaring at his aide.

"Call the staff," he spoke in clipped military manner. He never even saw the electrified women, though he crossed the room within inches of them, unconsciously brushing soapy water from his great barrel-like torso. "Get them here, Luis. At once."

The aide hastened away and Pancho continued to stride back and forth, thinking, and mumbling, and dripping. Then he became conscious of the women and held out a hand. One of them had the presence of mind to grab the nearest thing to a towel that was at hand, a pillow case. The other hastened into the bath for a real towel. Together they dried him as he walked, moving back and forth with him. He had begun to tousle his hair, massaging his scalp with powerful fingers. His lips moved a little but his eyes were almost glazed. He never quite realized that the two

143

women, sensible and service-minded as only good servants know how to be, dressed him completely then disappeared, all before the summoned staff could rush in. When his officers did arrive, they found an imposing General Villa standing erect, a plan of operation already in mind.

Because of reinforcements which Carranza had rushed to him, and because of new recruits which Pancho always attracted following any victory, he now had nearly 6,000 men under arms. Not all were well trained or well equipped. The enemy was sending approximately the same number to oust him from Juarez, his intelligence department informed him, and they *were* well trained, well equipped.

Pancho decided not to hole in at Juarez and wait for the Huerta forces to attack, for this would be bound to include much artillery pounding, with consequent fires and panic. Moreover, it was very likely to result in bullets crossing the Rio Grande, creating an "incident" which would be excuse enough for the American forces to intervene. Pancho wanted nothing that would offend the *gringos de Los Estados Unidos.*

"We do not have to defend Juarez inside Juarez itself," he told his staff. "We know the country of Chihuahua like the palms of our hands. The battle shall be at a place of our own choosing."

He was opening a map; he studied it a moment then pointed to an area near Tierra Blanca. All of his officers knew it to be virtually a desert with endless acres of soft Sahara-like sand. The enemy train would have to cross that. If it was stopped there, the wheels of its artillery would bog down when unloaded. An army must be mobile. Pancho's was so. His new and beloved Dorados, pick of all his men, had the best horses, but most of the others were mounted as well. Pancho despised the necessity of any fighting on foot but rose to heights of glory when astride almost any horse; a cavalryman, first and last. Around these facts he planned his strategy.

Wherefore, on that morning of November 21, 1913, General Villa ordered all his troops in Juarez to assemble in the street across from the railroad station, fully armed, equipped and dressed for "review." When they had so assembled he suddenly changed the order; they were not to show off, not to parade, but to march in all haste directly out of the city toward the south. No enemy spies could have read his mind or deduced his plan here. Only fifty men, under command of Juan N. Medina, were left to guard the town and conscript help as needed to send out food, arms, and ammunition.

On the sandy plains between Tierra Blanca and the railroad station of Bauche, Pancho deployed his main forces so as to have advantageous positions. One brigade under Jose Rodriguez, fifty men, formed the left wing. The artillery under Martiniano Servin and two more brigades under Villa and Toribio were in the center. The right wing was made up of the Juarez brigade under Aguirro Benavides. Here, they waited. Trains of the enemy were only four kilometers away.

When the surprised enemies learned that Villa was no longer in Juarez they became worried and wary. The Huerta commanders, Generals José Jesus Mancilla and Manuel Landa, held off while trying to decide what to do. They recognized that Villa had prepared himself for them. But they were encouraged by certain under-officers, especially Ines Salazar, Marcelo Caraveo, and Rafael Flores Alatorre, all men who had once followed Madero but turned traitor. Villa had expected the Huertistas to de-train and open fire in the early hours of November 23, but they did not. It was after nightfall of that day when the train headlights suddenly popped on and General Villa, watching intently from a hill not far away, heard the first burst of enemy artillery.

"Bueno, now we begin!" said he, exultantly. "But we do not rush. Not yet. This fight must go *our* way."

All through the night skirmishing took place, but no major charges. It was as if the Huerta forces were feeling Villa out. He refused to disclose his strength or probable intentions, he waited with the patience of an Indian.

At dawn he saw the Huerta cavalry move quickly and attack his right wing with great vigor; then another force attacked him on the left. Immediately it was a full-blown battle. The shouts of men were punctuated by bursts of cannon. Horses screaming from bullet wounds would plunge into the open, sending up geysers of sand that turned golden in the early sun. Acting under orders, and carefully watched, Villa's officers feinted time and again; thrust forward, drew back, nagging the enemy, tempting him, testing and taunting him. The enemy was stronger than Villa had hoped, and he soon realized that his old method of plunging headlong into battle would indeed have been disastrous here. Seasoned now, he played a wise and cautious game. All that day and night it lasted. On the next dawn fresh supplies arrived from Juarez; Medina had sent support as commanded.

This cautious fighting soon had precisely the effect that Pancho had hoped it would—it lured the opposing generals into believing that he was inadequately equipped and manned, hence too wary to attack. Wherefore they gleefully decided to start an all-out offensive of their own and end the matter immediately. Orders were given to leave positions near the train and charge at Villa's center, which they now considered weak.

It was not weak. It was, in truth, the trigger of a trap. Pancho, seeing the enemy approach, lifted his right arm. Across a little rocky valley from him an artillery sergeant watched him intently. When the arm swung down the sergeant barked a short command.

BOOM! . . . BOOM!

The thunder of shots from two large cannons roared over the battlefield. It was an enlargement of Pancho's arm signal, it was his prearranged command to spring out of hiding, leap to saddles, and follow him right up to the muzzles of the enemy's guns.

"EE-YAH-YAH-YAH-YAH-YAHA-A-A-!" That exuberant call to combat came from Pancho's throat. In the same moment his men saw him. Bullets by the thousands streaked at him like sleet in an Arctic storm, but he saw none and felt none, he leaned low in his saddle and charged.

Behind him at once his screaming battle cry was taken up by hundreds, the Dorados leading with their higher pitched "VIVA VI-I-I-I-I-LLA-A-A-A-A!" It was a shrieking wind. It was the moaning of a tempest. It was a chorus of vengeance from a hundred thousand peon souls, doomed by a cruel political system to a death of torture but reincarnated now in the persons of the men who charged.

Artillery shook the earth, rifles and machine guns rattled their nerve-chilling staccato, their bullets kicking up little puffs of sand like the first huge drops in an overture to rain. Nothing seemed to touch the racing, raging followers of Pancho Villa. In a moment the troops clashed head-on. Combat was violent, man to man, curse matching curse in unearthly fury. Villista horses, excited beyond control, leaped right at enemies' bayonets even as their riders swung their silvery sabres to cut off heads. It was

146

death and carnage at every turn, blood and carnage at every turn, blood and pain and violence such as none of them had ever seen before.

Villa's 6,000 felt zest for the action because here was their leader himself in the fastest, most dangerous part of the fighting, completely unafraid. The hottest blade was his, the deadliest pistols, and he seemed to be a target for a thousand guns. He should have been slain countless times. Was he truly a supernatural centaur, a phantom? A god, immune? Many peons thought so, and took inspiration from it. Many gave their own lives gloriously happy in the thought that they had died for Pancho Villa's cause, as indeed they had. The fighting covered acres, and quickly took on the aspects of a stampede with animals and men and smoke and dust and horror in a vast confusion.

It was not confusing to General Villa. It was a technique of terror which he had carefully planned and at which he was an experienced master. He noticed with pleasure that his banner bearers—young men, actually no more than boys—stayed near him, leaning low on their mounts for whatever protection that afforded, holding their staves with one hand and shooting pistols with the other. His buglers fought with sabres in right hands and horns in their left. It was incredible, it was terrifying, it was awesome to see and exhilarating to join.

Soon the Huerta flanks were broken and their center entirely chaotic; defeat loomed in all its magnitude. Pancho saw a frightful panic swell in Huerta's men. With screaming fiends on horseback literally cutting off their heads, arms, shoulders and legs with their bloody blades, the Huerta soldiers threw down their rifles and knelt to pray, or they plunged wildly in whatever direction seemed momentarily to promise safety.

There was no safety. There was just more danger, greater panic, for Pancho allowed them no respite. Many fled toward the waiting railroad trains. Most of those never reached the cars but fell victims of the blood-crazed Dorados. Some tried to bury themselves in sand and were trampled to death by horses. Others pretended to be dead, sprawled on the ground with their guns thrown away. They were promptly shot or hacked to death by plunging cavalrymen. Huerta's artillery cooled, no longer manned.

When Pancho, wild-eyed and grinning, saw that some enemy

soldiers had gotten back on their trains, he sent two lines of men down each side of the track. Even so, an engineer somehow got one locomotive started; his train began to move. From nowhere, then, appeared a Villista named Rudolfo Fierro. He had once been a brakeman. Pancho saw him race his horse a quarter mile to catch the train that was gathering speed, ignoring the bullets that rained around him. Fierro stood in his saddle and leaped to a platform. *Clank!* He swung a lever that put on the air brakes. The train screeched to a stop. His horse, trained to perfection, had stayed alongside so that Fierro leaped to his saddle again, shouted "VIVA VI-I-LLA-A-A!" and disappeared in a swirl of dust. The other cavalrymen were beside the train now, and of all the enemies who had tried to retreat on it not one was allowed to live.

The fighting ended more quickly than it had begun; action had stopped completely by 8 o'clock in the evening of November 25, 1913, though days were required for the surgery and the cleanup and the pyres. The Huerta forces had been completely annihilated. Pancho was almost hysterical with joy, for it had been the finest military action of his career.

That first great rush of Villa's Dorados, flanked by other mounted fighters whom he inspired, he knew would go down in the history of warfare as one of the great cavalry charges of all time.

16

WITHIN a week after his smashing victory there at Tierra Blanca, Pancho realized that his fame was now international, that his importance had soared as never before.

The fact disturbed him. He liked fame, yet feared it, and because of his trying to think through recent events, the old sense of confusion returned. Victory in the hills of Mexico was one thing, he told himself, but fame on three continents was another. He wasn't sure how to cope. On one day 1,200 letters were delivered to him, one-hundred-sixty of them from women proposing marriage. He had annihilated a Huerta army, killed and captured thousands of men, established himself definitely as the North American man of the year. Many of the marriage offers were from Americans, a few even from Canada. He saw more newspaper correspondents than ever swarm into his camp; he could hardly spit without creating a headline.

"General Villa rarely uses a toothbrush," one Yankee writer telegraphed New York, "yet his teeth are snow white and gleaming."

Pancho read that monumental triviality in a copy of the paper, and marveled at it, frowning. He wondered even more, frowned with still greater incomprehension when he began appearing in Mutt and Jeff and other comic strips of the period. Even when news reporters told him this was a distinction few men of any era could claim, he still didn't understand.

He realized that his comeback after capture and escape was an affront to many prominent Mexicans, and that fact pleased him, for he felt simply that right had triumphed. But his comeback also pleased thousands of others, including many Mexicans of high education and rank. After all, a newsman told Pancho, success is irresistible; it bridges almost any social or economic barrier.

Among those who joined him after the victory was Felipe Angeles, and two persons of more divergent backgrounds could hardly have been imagined. Each had heard much of the other. Friends had told Pancho that Angeles was an Academy officer who had completed higher studies in the French Army. When the two shook hands, each was modest. They appraised one another with disarming frankness, and Pancho liked the newcomer at once.

"You are a big man physically, General Villa," said Angeles, smiling. "I envy you, sir. You must be very strong."

"I am strong, yes. And whiter skinned than you. White Spanish. Many people say I am Indian, but it is not so. You are part Indian, maybe? You are bronzed."

"Probably. If so, I am proud of it."

"Of a certainty, yes. If you are Indian you will have more sympathy for unfortunate peons. Most peons are dark like you, or darker. You are taller than most. Thin, too, Señor Angeles. And you have an even temper, sir? Me, I am mean. Too mean.

I get mad and am very dangerous, even to myself. You could help me control that, *señor*."

Angeles smiled again. "Any man who confesses his meanness is not inherently mean, General."

Pancho sighed, and led the new man to camp chairs before a table, but when an orderly brought drinks, both declined. "I get mad and shoot people, sir. I have to be hard. You understand? I could not command many rough men and mean soldiers without being mean at times myself. I do not alibi for my temper. I do regret that I am not educated enough to command in any other way."

They talked in this vein for two hours, asking many questions, probing one another's minds and souls. Pancho enjoyed it. Neither asked for anything nor expected it, but toward the end Pancho said, "It would be a wonderful thing for the army of freedom if you could fight at my side, Señor Angeles. If you were where I could talk with you often."

Angeles stood up and bowed. "General, it would be an honor for me. If I may consider your thought an invitation, I hereby accept."

The suddenness of that acceptance surprised Pancho, and delighted him. It was as if he had an unexpected friend to lean on; someone vaguely comparable to his well-remembered mother, to whom he had looked as a child.

He gave thought to that when alone again. *Why* do I get homesick ever so often, he asked himself. There are times when I want to give up all this tearing around the country fighting and killing and pillaging, and at such times I need a good friend to talk to quietly. A wife, maybe? No. A wife is a woman, not a friend.

The famous general sighed deeply, loosened his collar, rumpled his thick black hair—and ordered food.

As always when disturbed, he ate heavily, slowly, prodigiously. The food, red meat especially, seemed to beget a tranquilizing lethargy in him so that he could stretch out and relax. But it or the abundance of *agua miel* (sweet water, from the maguey or century plant) that went down with the food, also forced him out of bed every hour or so, thus disturbing his rest.

After one such trip to the toilet he came back to bed and lay with hands locked under his head for a half hour, thinking. A sure instinct told him that he had now achieved more than bandit

150

notoriety, he had suddenly shouldered a huge national responsibility. He was being called the great *insurrecto*, and for good reason. But this knowledge brought him no elation.

"Be damned!" he murmured. He often reverted to English when using profanity, though his was always mild. "Angeles say I go down in history. All I want is to kick out the rich slaveholders, then go to a quiet farm somewhere. I do not want to be in history."

But man does not choose his own destiny, he realized; he makes it unwittingly. Pancho Villa had built up a momentum that couldn't be slowed.

It accelerated rapidly in the next few months. Much of this was due to Felipe Angeles. Pancho was happy to let Felipe gradually take over most of the heavy thinking, the strategy, the political planning and maneuvering, for he himself felt incapable there. Felipe thus was made counsellor as well as artillery commander, and later organized the Villa infantry since, up to now, most that Pancho had commanded had been cavalry.

Pancho soon agreed with Felipe that they must coordinate their military efforts with those of Carranza, another rising star. After all, Carranza was the commander-in-chief, Felipe pointed out; Villa and Carranza thus should confer.

"For one thing," said Felipe, "rumors are going around that you want to replace Carranza, and that he wants to assassinate you. You know how people talk, my friend."

"Hah! Foolish talk. I will go to Carranza myself. Now!"

But the interview was a complete failure. General Villa came back snapping mad.

"The son of a beech!" he snarled to a *gringo* newsman, who was obviously delighted to have such a scoop interview. "Carranza and me, we don' get along. You know w'at he say, amigo?"

"What, sir?"

"He say—hah!—that notheeng is to be promise the poor people. Hells to Betsy, is w'at I fight for! Is the whole theeng!"

"*Seguro si*, General. But what will you do then?"

Pancho turned to the reporter, still glaring in anger. "Me, I go—how you say him?—I paddle my own canoose, thass w'at I do."

He started by approaching the important city of Torreon. For this effort he now had about 8,000 trained troops plus 2,000 new volunteers picked up as he neared the city. His artillery was commanded by his new-found friend, Felipe Angeles. Pancho had already designated him as a general. Together the two men decided that the way to take Torreon was in knife-like thrusts at night—dash in, fight furiously, withdraw, dash in at another place.

It became a bloody business, as any knifing does. After eleven days of continuous struggle, one by one the Torreon advance posts began to fall until Villa reached the city's main suburban points of defense—Tlahualilo, Bermejillo, Mapimi. These were finally taken. More heavy fighting took place before he captured Huarache Canyon, and again in the Calabazas, Santa Rosa, and Polvorera hills; but from here on General Angeles' artillery had control of the city. One of the bloodiest combats was in and around the fort on Pila hill, a key position. Slowly and progressively the Villistas then took the communities of Sacramento, Lardo, and Gomez Palacio, the latter at the very city limits of Torreon. Now they were in position to make strong frontal attack, Pancho decided.

This became even more costly, Pancho discovered to his dismay. He found that General Jose Refugio Velazco, defending Torreon, had a strong force and was himself capable. Villa sent wave after wave against his guns. Both sides suffered terrible losses. Finally, Villa's advance troops, inspired by the shrieking, sabre swinging Dorados, forced their way into the Torreon Park and city market. General Velazco sent an officer out under a white flag.

"We ask that a truce be called for twenty-four hours," that emissary said, "so that both sides may pick up its wounded and bury the dead."

"Request refused," snapped Villa. "Get back to Velazco before I cut your guts out." It was not an idle threat; message bearers from enemies commonly were slain, and Pancho well knew it. He saw the man's tearful gratitude. Pancho had learned that reinforcements for Velazco were on the way. If a day's truce should be arranged, time would change the whole situation.

Pancho therefore ordered an all-out charge at once. His artillery began to vomit their loads with redoubled ferocity. He himself galloped out at the head of charging troops, ignoring their cries of protests. Again he and his horse seemed immune to bullets and death. He was sure he had been recognized by the enemy, and

152

that every gun in range must have been turned on him at times. But he rode like a shadow in the wind, giving his strong personal inspiration to the battleweary men, telling them what to do and showing them how to do it even in the very jaws of death. Only when a group of his officers surrounded him and restrained him bodily (and at considerable risk to themselves) was he held back. These took heart from him and began to lead ferocious attacks. Defending troops soon grew discouraged.

The break came on April 2, 1914, during dramatic sound and action supplied by nature. This whole of central Mexico is a vast stage set, and Pancho in quieter hours had oftened admired it. Impressionistic hills of purple thrust themselves irrationally out of golden plains, peaks loomed in majesty that made shivering insects of men.

Into the sunshine here, General Villa first saw cosmic children come out for play—little *remolinos*, dust devils chasing one another over the horizons. Within an hour they seemed to lock hands and acquire a giant-like ferocity, whizzing over the landscape, lifting sand and gravel that buffed the very paint off buildings and all but blinded animals and men. Shielding his eyes, he heard rather than saw the fighting stop because nobody could see to shoot, much less distinguish friend from foe. Nervous horses stampeded; other groups of them humped their backs, hung their heads, and shut their eyes to weather it out.

Villa knew that his men were glad of the momentary respite; glad to interrupt the carnage; grateful for an hour or so in which to restore nerves and soul, even though visibility was no farther than five or six feet, often barely an arm's length. Many sat with scarves or any available fabric over their noses, straining the air. Papers, boxes, straw sombreros by the hundreds, trash and banners and anything loose swept across the country in fantastic flight parade.

Pancho never understood how any sort of order could be carried out, how men and horses could move with any surety at all. But covered by this great blinding blow, the defenders of Torreon retreated.

Next morning General Villa led his victorious army sedately but happily down Torreon's beautiful but battle-bloodied streets. Immediately behind his crack cavalrymen came General Angeles and the artillery. Weary men had worked most of the night shining up their guns, grooming their horses, cleansing themselves. Their eyes were bleary with fatigue, yet their steps were lively as they marched. This was their reward—the victory parade always was the reward after battle in Mexico. One can sleep any time, but thus to march before a conquered enemy—ah ha, my friends, it is something, eh? Both sides respected the custom. American newsmen riding with Villa said they could hardly believe it. He had beaten a great and proud city to its knees, yet here a few hours later were its own citizens waving flags and cheering him with their "VIVA'S," throwing him kisses and red roses as if he were merely a popular matador preparing to enter this afternoon's bull ring. Viva Villa. Villa the *liberador*. Villa, a magic name. The conqueror found himself beaming in benevolence as he rode along.

The Battle of Torreon had great significance, Pancho soon learned. It meant that Huerta's strongest defensive armies had been crushed, for no other place had been so well fortified. Pancho explained to newspaper reporters that General Angeles, on capturing Gomez Palacio, had obtained a map which showed the city's fortifications; thus his cannons had been able to pierce right into vital points. Defeat of the federal army was the plainest possible demonstration of Villa's tenacity and military power, he was told.

When the quiet moments came again, the lull after carnage, he took once more to his bed, not in illness but in emotional exhaustion, still trying to think out his own personal position in the new life. He didn't like what he discovered. This was Success, to be sure, but somehow it was unsavory; fame was a spiritual fraud.

He groaned, forced himself out of bed, and ordered food.

17

An hour after he had finished his big meal this time, General Francisco Villa suddenly jumped from his bed, ran out of his headquarters tent, and vomited in a most unmilitary manner. He sounded like the retching of a dog that had found poisoned meat. He himself thought he was dying.

"I go now," said he, to no one but himself.

Then he stumbled back inside and dropped onto the sheets again, hoping only to die in peace. When he actually felt better fifteen minutes later, he was embarrassed.

"Be damn!" he muttered, sitting blearily on the side of his bed.

He stripped naked and once more walked to the inevitable stream near which he had camped. Once more the bathing restored him, physically.

He came out hungry for a woman. An aide, having no difficulty discovering that fact, whispered a crisp order to a guard, who quietly passed it on. General Villa paid them no attention; his mind was whirling a little, but slowly focusing on new military plans. Thus he was surprised that night to come into his private tent and instantly detect a heavenly perfume. The light in here had been dimmed. A full minute passed before he discovered the girl in his bed waiting, smiling, eager.

He spoke no word to her. None was needed. He never even knew her name, nor cared if he didn't. He fell asleep afterward—that was about 11 p.m.—and rested deeply, thoroughly, until almost noon next day. When he awoke, he was a new man again.

"Felipe," he said to that trusted friend and helper, "we have to capture Zacatecas."

"Yes, I know," General Felipe Angeles nodded. "You have been planning, and so have I. But we are bucking a mountain this time. Zacatecas will be no little ranch hacienda, sir."

"You know the city well?"

Felipe nodded. "I have gotten every detail we need to know. It is a mining center, on the great central plateau of Mexico. Elevation 4,500 feet. Surrounded by beautiful hills, each now strongly fortified."

"Ah. With cannons." Pancho had begun to study a large map.

"Grillo Hill is the key position, General. Its cannons could tear out our guts unless we silence them first. We have forty cannons of our own."

"We are Villistas!" Pancho's old pride was rising again. "And we number 21,000 men. But we will hold 7,000 in reserve, eh? Then we go at them like this—"

He outlined his plan and it was a good one. But Felipe urged extreme caution and care, so Zacatecas was thoroughly reconnoitered again. Then at proper time, Pancho ordered advance patrols to make thrusts that felt out the defenders, but no heavy attack was made for many hours. He was patient, sensing the correct moment for each move as only a seasoned leader could, striding back and forth, going out to touch his privates who all but worshipped him. Infantry and cavalry units were carefully placed, under cover of night.

"Take the reserves," Pancho ordered, "and hide them along the railroad. If the enemy tries to escape, it will be that way."

On June 23, 1914, when every detail was complete, General Villa gave the signal for his cannon to open fire.

They did so with such bursts and such accuracy that the defenders were disheartened that first hour. The outlying hills were ineffectual guardians. Grillo fell in bloody assault. Villa watched every move, and at the psychological moment ordered his strong infantry to attack. With defenders crowded to the limit, his Dorados led the inevitable cavalry charge. The timing was perfect.

When his enemies were forced out of the defending hills, it quickly became apparent that they could not long hold the city proper. As Villa had predicted, they tried to escape by the way of railroad south to Aguascalientes. His reserves were right there fresh and eager for the kill. He watched the carnage with steely eyes, a warrior without feelings.

The battle took less than nine hours. Yet the rout was so complete that only one hundred riders escaped. All the other defending soldiers were either killed, wounded, or taken prisoner. Fighting on the Zacatecas-Guadalupe road had been so furious that for a distance of six miles nobody could pass without stumbling over the bodies of dead men and horses. Pancho learned that twenty-two mine shafts and wells had been filled with corpses, then covered with stones. Still there were more, so he ordered great trenches dug, the dead dragged and tossed into them like garbage, doused with oil and set fire.

All of that night he rode back and forth, Satan astride a black horse. The countryside was a scene from Dante, lesser devils carrying bodies of men to the pyres, their forms silhouetted against the flames, their shadows stretching up the slopes and weaving in a ghastly dance of death. Pancho saw grimly that the odors of burning flesh made such a stench that many of his

156

Villistas, though reduced now to mad devils indeed, retched and fainted from the sheer revolting horror of it.

Few battles in any country's history had ever ended with such complete and significant annihilation of the enemy, American newspaper reporters told Pancho. He himself truly looked like a creature from hell, and felt it. But soon after dawn, the letdown began. He yearned for an end of horror. Once he covered his face with huge hands and forced himself to envision the tender smile of his mother, long dead. It was comforting, it enabled him to regain control. He wished with all his heart that he had a peaceful farm he could now go to and live there forever.

He was still despondent three days later, and his friend Felipe ventured to comfort him. "You need a rest, General. Maybe a fishing trip, or a little wild game hunting. How about that?"

Pancho shook his head. "I have killed enough."

Felipe, sensitive and intelligent, gripped his friend's shoulders. "Do not blame yourself, Pancho. We all get caught up in the stream of events."

Pancho looked long and sadly at him. "I wanted only to free my mother and her children, my little sisters, my brothers. No no, I suppose I wanted an end to all peon slavery. Of course I did. But I have killed many thousands of the very peons I tried to help. In bloody battles, Felipe! Blood and horror. I will go to hell."

He saw Felipe stare wonderingly at him for a long moment, then he forced himself to smile.

"Pay no attention to me, Felipe. I am just tired, is all. Tired of fighting. I am getting to be an old man before my time, eh?"

He laughed gently at the feeble little joke, and felt better for it. He inhaled deeply, stretched his arms high, pounded his chest.

"Hah!" he exclaimed in forced heartiness. "Enough of this baby talk. We have work to do, General Angeles. Our men must be comforted and praised. We must keep up the good work we have started, eh, my friend?"

Two weeks passed. It was enough to regroup, reconsider old and new military plans. It was also enough to recover from the shock of carnage. He still felt scarred inside, but he felt physically renewed, and knew that the juices in him were running strong again. These were old symptoms in him and he recognized them for what they were, a recurrent hunger for sex. It was both annoying and exhilarating. A man ought to settle down with *one* good woman, eh? Enjoy her and watch her raise his children. He found that thought very appealing—and marveled at himself for it. He hadn't often been like that. He dismissed the idea.

Two days later it was necessary for him and his staff to make a train trip. The train stopped at the town of Ortiz to refuel and Pancho got off to stretch his legs. As he walked up and down the platform he came to a group of young ladies who had been waiting for the train because someone had told them they might glimpse the famous general. They did not know him by sight, and he was not in uniform as he approached, so he overheard them talking.

"They say he is a rapist," one girl declared, in awed tones.

"I bet he is a good lover, even so," another suggested.

"But Lupe, that Pancho is a murderer and a bandit! He does all sorts of horrid things."

"And rape is worst of all," the first insisted.

That's when the strange man stopped near her and spoke.

"Do you know this Pancho, *señorita?*" he asked.

"No *señor*. But they say of him that—"

"Hah! They say everything of him. Young lady, *I* am Pancho Villa!"

He saw the girls turn white with fear, then he reached out and grasped the first one by the arm, she who had called him a rapist. He called to an aide.

"Put her on the train," he ordered. "She needs an education."

The other girls began an instant pleading for her, and because the incident had attracted several men, they too dared object. He ignored all of them. He followed the captive girl onto the train and said to her, "I have to teach you a lesson. You see, you don't know me, yet you declare I am a very bad person."

Felipe Angeles, the only man who ever dared actually defy Pancho, came up then. "What are you doing, man?" he demanded. "You can't abduct a girl this way!"

"I am not 'abducting.' You talk without knowledge, Felipe. This girl has been saying bad things about Pancho Villa when I had no bad intentions whatsoever. So, she shall have a good education then be returned to her town to tell the truth."

He sent a telegram to Chihuahua City and asked a friend and his wife to meet the train. The girl was turned over to them. It developed that she was an orphan, and so under Pancho's patronage this couple cared for her and gave her an education at the general's expense, right on through a college degree. Thus years later Señorita Pepa Valdez returned to her home town of Ortiz as one of Pancho Villa's strongest defenders. Never did he even suggest to her any form of romance between them, but he discovered that the summary abduction did make meat for his enemies' propaganda mill. It was dramatized all over Mexico as a fiendish, lecherous act. It did more than any other incient to give Pancho Villa a bad name.

During the next six months or so he had to watch with horror and frustration while an intricate political intrigue against him developed. It was so complex that even American newspapers began contradicting themselves without realizing it, he learned. Changes in alliances would occur between dinner and breakfast, so that morning editions of papers would contradict afternoon editions, and readers could be no less than confused. Not even the Mexican people could follow it though they were pawns in the matter. (And down the years, equally conscientious historians trying to untangle it have ended up with different conclusions.)

Explanation of it actually was very simple, Pancho soon discovered; several opportunists arose, each wanting a share of Villa's riches and fame. Under the guise of patriotism they would do anything, and so "loyalty" was sold and resold by the hour to the highest bidder.

Pancho Villa tried repeatedly to retire from it completely. He developed a sense of disgust. He announced that "I'm through. I will go buy a small ranch somewhere and raise cattle as a forgotten man."

He found that he couldn't do it. All his generals rallied to keep him, in spite of many enemies large and small. He was literally forced to struggle in the web of intrigue.

Then late in 1914 when Carranza finally made triumphal entry into Mexico City as commander-in-chief of the Constitutionalist Army, Pancho had a feeling of relief. Perhaps now he could know some peace. Huerta, his old enemy, had fled for his life to a foreign country. Maybe Carranza would settle down.

It was a forlorn hope, but there was an interval of waiting and watching. During this, Pancho's mind reverted to one of its old channels. He felt a craving, not just for any woman this time, but specifically for the one to whom he felt most married, Luz Corral de Villa. It was a wistful sort of yearning, in truth. That a man could go so far in achievement, that he could know international renown, that he could have the highest possible patriotic ideals while simultaneously being a lecherous centaur, and all the while be a victim of a genuine love, was a sad fact of Pancho Villa's life and character, and he himself said so to his friend Felipe Angeles. Then he sought out Luz. He found her again without much trouble, though to avoid publicity he went to her at night.

"You have changed, Luz," said he, when he had held her close once more. He spoke rather sadly. "It is in your eyes, your face."

"Pancho, I am older."

"Older, hah! I'm the one who is old."

"*You* will never be. I honestly think you will be boyish at sixty, Pancho. But me—the change in my face is due to wrinkles. My skin is not the sweet blush of mountain apples, as you once said of it. You remember that?"

"I remember." He sat down. He somehow felt disappointed, wished he hadn't come. Luz Corral de Villa stirred no response in him, no eagerness. Too late he realized that his mind had been searching for a phantom, an elusive hope maybe, a yearning for a happier time and place. But he looked at Luz, wistfully, gently. She in turn was gentle with him; tender and reserved. He could tell that she recognized the gulf separating them. More sad than when he came, he left her and returned to his command.

Again and again Villa announced that he did not want to rule Mexico, and insisted that no military leader be allowed to sit in the president's chair. This, he learned, endeared him to the public, even in the United States. It attracted literally thousands of Mexico's most distinguished statesmen, educators, scientists, and attorneys to his support. He became a heroic champion of peace and order. But it did not endear him to Carranza, especially when he issued a manifesto denouncing that self-made dictator and calling on the people to repudiate him and elect a temporary president whom the Villistas could support. Friction between those two continued to grow during that Autumn of 1914. Meanwhile yet another hopeful had quietly risen to importance on the military scene of Mexico—Emiliano Zapata. Because he opposed Carranza, Villa supported him.

160

During this high-level time of his career, General Villa built a mansion for himself and Luz at Chihuahua City, then spent most of his time in a deluxe private train. (The house still stands, its stone entry arrogantly protruding right to the middle of Tenth Street, most of its rooms now unfurnished but open day and night for any penniless peon family in from the farms and needing a place to camp.) Pancho had hoped the mansion would prove his stability, especially to himself. He hoped he could find the will power to retire here and settle down in peaceful obscurity. But that was a passing mood, he discovered; a whim of the moment. Some new stimulus came along and he was snorting fire again.

Meanwhile, too, the economics of leadership, as well as the military demands, had assailed him. He decided to do what the Confederate rebels had done in America, issue paper money. An energetic young paper salesman from Phoenix, Arizona, went to Chihuahua City and sold the mighty Pancho carloads of Oriole Bond from the Graham Paper Company of St. Louis. Because he was personable and astute, Villa took to him and a friendship ripened.

"You sell paper," Pancho sighed in one conversation. "Yet I tell you wars are won by the sword, not by the pen, no matter what your poets says, Señor Estam—Estam—."

"Stambaugh," the man supplied, for the hundredth time. "Charlie Stambaugh."

"Hell of a name, *amigo*. I make you a general, eh? I give you a batter name. A seemple Mexican name, like General Carlos Estampillos de la Bustamente de la Peralta de la Marinez y Arango—hah! You like the name Arango, my fran'? I make you 'General Doroteo Arango.' I give you a beeg white horse, two peestols, a sword, a—"

"Just give me a safe passage back to civilization, *amigo*," begged Charlie, and big Pancho laughed with the volume of a bellowing bull. He enjoyed needling his friends, especially the Americans. Because he liked Charlie "Arango" he paid him for the carloads of paper not in the paper money made from them, but in that money Americans always loved—gold.

During a rather long interval now, Pancho was forced to look at Mexican politics. He did so with his guard up, frankly admitting he didn't know what the high hopping hades was going on and didn't really care, so long as the poor people of Mexico weren't enslaved by it.

"Me, I'd rather go feeshing," he grinned to a Yankee newshawk.

"I know what you mean, General. Between you and me, I think you are fed up with your Mexican revolution. The drama is going a little stale, *no es verdad?*"

"*Seguro si.* You are esmart. *amigo.* But—" The big general shrugged. "I cannot always boss theengs. You onderstan'?"

The reporter nodded in sympathy. "All too well, sir."

He learned that the Constitutionalist leaders would hold a grand convention in the City of Aguascalientes in October of 1914, and that his presence was expected. He heard how it took on many aspects of a grand opera, with plots and counterplots, charges and countercharges, resignations and reinstatements. Pancho stayed away as long as he could, then he was drafted.

Once there, he opened his heart and made the most significant speech of his career. The newsmen told him so, and he knew it was true. He was illiterate but fiery, with an enthusiasm that was electric, contagious. Half the big auditorium was reduced to tears by it. He led it to melodramatic climax when all the leaders stood hands-over-hearts and made pledges of loyalty, then passed by a table to write their names indelibly on a Mexican flag.

In return, General Antonio I. Villareal addressing the convention turned dramatically to Pancho and said, "You, General Villa, are the real heart of the people's revolution. You are fragile as glass to weep, yet strong as iron to resist and fight. That is why we all understand and praise your tenderness and your military achievements. Because in your good heart, General Villa, we discover the emotion with which our countrymen suffer their pains, and in the strength of you we recognize the courage of our people to fight against injustice."

The applause was thunderous for half an hour. Pancho, proud, was reduced to tears, sobbing openly.

Another incident spotlighted him anew. It was in a cantina one afternoon of the Convention. For relaxation, General Villa had walked out of the big hall and down the street, just sunning and stretching. He came to some children playing, and one of them had a trained pig on a little rope.

"Hola! What have we here, *muchachos?*" called the great man, heartily.

They had no knowledge of his identity or importance, but some dozens of adults had followed him and more watched as he walked along. He squatted cowboy fashion on one heel to pet the pig.

"He is named Little Red Devil, *señor*," the owner of the pig, a boy, answered. "He will squeal if you tickle his ear, and grunt if you give him a bite to eat."

"Hah! Good afternoon, Little Red Devil. Let me hold you, eh?"

The big handsome man cuddled the piglet in his arms. It seemed happy there, as a kitten would. Pancho was delighted.

"Luis!" he called.

That ever-present shadow materialized at Pancho's elbow again. Pancho strode away with the pig while Luis distributed golden coins to all the children. It is doubtful if ever a pig, before or since, was sold for as much as Little Red Devil.

The adult audience had grown to smiling hundreds, and those who could crowd in followed Pancho into a cantina bar. He himself did not drink. He never did, beyond *agua miel*, the harmless sweet water, except on rare occasions. But now he ordered a baby's bottle and nipple and, while the public watched, taught Little Red Devil to suck beer. It became a major event. It made talk. It made headlines. It made Pancho Villa more down-to-earth than ever in the eyes of the people. He left the piglet as a mascot of the saloon and it grew to happy hogdom there, finally was butchered for charity.

News of the pig, along with news of the big Convention, spread over Mexico and lifted Pancho higher than ever in the public mind, much to the dismay of Carranza. That ambitious one had hoped to slip into Huerta's presidential chair even before it had time to cool. But Villa's pressures were too strong, and the Convention had named General Eulalio Gutierrez as president *pro tem*, still hoping Pancho would take the job. Carranza, biding his time, withdrew his troops from Mexico City and himself fled to Vera Cruz. Then he quietly formed an alliance with the man Pancho had once had an impulse to kill—Obregon.

The interim gave Villa opportunity to reach the highest peak of his career. Feeling elated and zestful again, on December 6,

1914, he as commander-in-chief of the Revolutionary armies marched triumphantly into the national capital, Mexico City.

He had led other parades elsewhere, had heard the cheers of the populace before. All of that was bare prologue to the ovation accorded him here. He rode along smiling, waving, saluting, and feeling grand. He went past the very buildings where he had once been imprisoned, but he had no time for bitter memories. Cannons boomed, bands blared their exultant melodies, he watched the multitude become a screaming, hysterical, fiesta-minded mob. He rode in a car beside the president, but that gentleman went unrecognized.

"Villa, Villa, Villa, Villa, VILLA, VILLA, VILLA!"

The cry became a rhythmic chanting that swelled into thunder over the capital's beautiful streets. The car could hardly move through the surging human sea. He stood bareheaded on the back seat, lifting both arms, saluting, waving, smiling, bowing, acknowledging the overwhelming tribute. He could not talk, he was too choked with emotion. This was Victory, he felt; this outpouring showed a united Mexico anxious to dedicate itself to economic and spiritual growth.

During his first few days in the city, photographers and newspaper men swarmed around him. He even posed, at their request, sitting in the presidential chair, but he made quite a joke of this, saying that if he actually were president he would issue two executive commands: (1) All members of his cabinet should be beautiful women, and (2) all newspaper men should be tossed into the fiery maw of Popocatapetl. Yet when they tightened him down to a serious talk, he astonished them with his interest and insight into governmental affairs. He knew they had always thought of him as the gay caballero—which indeed he could be; and that now many found it hard to accept his deeper, dedicated side, or to understand just why he was not amassing a personal fortune or securing a dictatorship for himself. He sensed that they did not really know the highly complex character of Pancho Villa. But then, who did? Villa himself didn't understand Villa. He felt his old confusion recurring.

He conferred at length with President Gutierrez and other officials, then news came that he was needed again at the head of his troops. He welcomed this escape. A centaur accustomed to galloping across the plains and the wild free hills is never likely

164

to be happy corralled in a government building, he told newsmen
in hearty farewell.

18

THE GREAT Republic of Mexico could settle down now that Villa
had entered the capital—so Pancho was told by American newsmen. "Your dream has achieved substance at last, General," one
said to him. "Your ideal is close to realization. You can be proud."
   "Hah! I can be wary!"
Pancho already had seen the upsurge of little jealousies and
intrigues, from a host of ambitious men seeking personal gain.
He also realized that Mexico was now divided between two talen-
ted generals of the Revolution—Zapata to the south of Mexico
City, and he himself controlling the vast area to the north.
   That division of strength and command was disastrous, he
slowly learned. Many more battles were fought; and, because of
the restrictions on him, Villa lost most of the important ones.
   Yet in each case he bounced back. The name of Villa held its
magic, and with Felipe Angeles at his side he became skilled at
regrouping and reorganization. Again and again he refused the
blandishments of promoters who would have made him president
of Mexico. He did not want that, he insisted; he wanted freedom
for the peons, and peace for all. He personally was more than
willing to retire.
   "I am not educated," he explained over and over, with complete
sincerity. "I do not know how to rule a nation, I know only how
to fight and how to make love to women." Few men have been
more honest, an American reporter said.
   No retirement was possible, especially when in its inimitable
way the United States again "butted in" on affairs of a sister
republic, as Pancho and others viewed it.
   President Woodrow Wilson, greatly alarmed now anyway by a
new war in Europe, was in a dither about which faction in Mexico his government should recognize. Unfortunately, Carranza got
in his licks first. He sent a man from Pasadena, California, to

Washington as his emissary. The man was Richard H. Cole, who had lived for twenty-six years in Mexico. It is tragic that his knowledge of Mexican developments was limited, and more tragic that he was accepted by Washington.

"What the flaming hell does *Señor* Cole know about Mexico?" roared Pancho Villa. "What if he did live here once? He is not here now, and knows nothing of our plans."

General Villa tried every way he knew to prevent the recognition of Carranza. He went to El Paso and conferred with General Hugh L. Scott, Chief of the Military Staff of the American Army, who offered to support him. Scott then personally asked Wilson not to recognize Carranza, then had to tell Pancho he had failed. Wilson's government gave its nod of approval to Carranza on October 15, 1915. Pancho pounded his desk and literally sobbed in frustration. He had been America's friend.

That stab in the back meant also that Villa could get no more arms, ammunition, and supplies from the United States. It meant that Francisco Villa, who had risen to such heights that he could *refuse* a presidency, was in American eyes reduced to the status of outlaw again.

"It would not be so sad," he confessed to a reporter friend, "if Carranza was any sort of patriot."

"Ignorance is humanity's greatest curse, Pancho," the wise friend replied. "Even a president in Washington can be ignorant of what goes on here."

"He is a son of a beech." Pancho reverted to his favorite profanity in English, one taught him by the news correspondents.

"So. And quite a few people agree with you. But that doesn't help us now."

As his political affairs grew worse, so did his personal ones. He found trusted men deserting him like the proverbial rats from a ship. His truly close friend, Felipe Ángeles, had gone to the United States to try to prevent the Carranza recognition, and had been unable to return. Others reasonably close to him either just disappeared or boldly went over to the enemy. One old faithful was lost by accident. This was Rodolfo Fierro, the firebrand Dorado who had once been a railroad brakeman.

Fierro's legend in Mexico became in some ways comparable to that of Villa himself; in fact, many evil deeds charged against Pancho Villa were actually the doings of his henchman, Fierro.

166

It was the latter, newsmen reminded the world, who once raced horseback to catch a train of retreating enemies, jumped to a car platform, applied the brakes, and escaped unhurt in a shower of bullets. Down the years it was Fierro who became chief executioner for Villa. He could kill prisoners with no more compunction than a housewife might show at wringing a chicken's neck. He actually seemed to enjoy slaughter of his fellow man, and such a nerveless individual can be valuable to the commander-in-chief of an army, Pancho discovered. But the Villistas lost Fierro one day near Casas Grandes. The rural folk near there had a habit of digging big, deep wells in the dry beds of lakes during seasons of drouth, thus finding emergency water. Then when rains came again, the wells filled and were invisible under the lakes' few feet of water.

One day Fierro and some companions were riding single file across one of the lakes that had water in it now, when Fierro's horse suddenly dropped from sight. Man and beast just disappeared and were never seen again; one of the submerged wells had claimed them. Pancho felt both shock and relief; he had feared Fierro.

A long series of these personal losses drove Pancho once more to seek solace from women. In a prolonged spree he "married" at least two, yet he courted with all the ingratiating charm of a college lad when he had a mood to. If refused by a girl, he pined away for a few hours or even days, apparently forgetting that he could and did simply take other desired things by force. He often heard or read of himself being accused of rape, but in not one single instance was he guilty of it. On the contrary, time after time he "abducted" girls on sudden fancy, found them so irrevocably frightened or unwilling that he sent them back to their homes with lavish gifts including money, their bodies untouched.

"Why force yourself on any woman?" he himself loftily asked it. "Just stand there smiling and they force themselves on you!" There was and still is much truth in that conceited masculine dictum, especially in Mexico.

Among the truly good women that Pancho "married" after due courtship, even to the formal asking for her hand in a conference with her parents, was one named Librada. He had discovered a basic refinement that shone in her delicate features, her fair skin and long, luxurious hair; she did not show the animal-like earthiness of the peons. He realize that she knew relatively little of his "bad" side when she fell in love with him, though she must have known that she was not his only woman. He felt a love for her which was above the sordid, above the physical, and he showered much gentleness on Librada. He bought her gifts, he spoke kindly to her, he took her riding in a fine automobile, he showed her what nine-tenths of all husbands in all lands never show or which they lose much too soon—gallantry. She became the mother of some of the children who were to enrich his last tragic years. Yet of her, too, he soon tired; if tired is the word. Who knows just why a man puts any woman aside, marches off to war, and comes back with another? Pancho Villa had to ask himself that very question, and he found no answer.

Circumstances meanwhile had forced Villa back into his old region, the northern hills and plains. There was some comfort in being on familiar ground, but there was no rest; the remnants of Revolutionary armies that he gathered had much bloody combat in store. He was bitter because his once grand "ally", the United States of America, now had to be considered an ally of his enemies. The United States allowed his enemy's generals to use its ships, its trains, its ammunition and material.

One big battle became a show for the *gringos* themselves, he discovered, since it was right on the international line. In November of 1915 he threw his thinning, desperate Villistas against the town of Agua Prieta, Sonora, just south of Douglas, Arizona. He found it unexpectedly fortified with that relatively new defensive weapon, barbed wire. This completely nullified his famed Dorados, cavalrymen given heretofore to picturesque charges that often turned a battle's tide. When he turned his artillary lose to destroy the barbed wire, the bursts merely scattere the stuff in a different and still dangerous pattern, while adding shell holes that were themselves a menace to horses. When he waited for the cover of night, a thousand or more powerful American spotlights illuminated both horsemen and infantrymen, blinding them and making easy targets.

"The damned *gringos* have betrayed us!" he cried over and over. "May their entrails rot in the belly of hell!"

Villa was forced to flee from Agua Prieta, leaving a trail of his own dead and dying. He had come there at a great cost anyway, marching his men across the vast expanses of Mexico, lugging

168

heavy cannon, rationing food and seeing fatigue sap the strength of his men, while Obregon the enemy general used the American railroad to transport his soldiers in comparative luxury. Much prolonged fighting-on-the-run ensued. The Sonoran campaign became a fast and bloody one.

"I do not find the time even to make the love, *señores*," Pancho ranted at his now few American newspaper friends. "When I come into a pretty girl, what I do? I get off my horse, I bow to her, I esmile. Then—BOOM—some fool eshoot a cannon after me, hah!"

He made a big joke of it, but he knew it was no joking matter, he did truly have to run. He fought back and forth, trying always to consolidate his forces and make something of an efficient army. But American General Frederick Funston gave permission for Villa's enemies to use American trains. Supplies ran low. Men grew hungry and discouraged. In short, Villa saw his Sonoran campaign a complete failure. He became an object of ridicule, so fickle is fame. Carranza's propagandists kept pouring grist into their mills, Pancho observed bitterly. General Francico Villa, the great friend of the American people just a few months ago, found himself bandit Villa again and without the original bandit's happy-go-lucky glamor; the sooner this Villa was exterminated, the better. So ranted the American press.

When he took stock he found that he had a scant six hundred men where once he had commanded many thousands, and these few were at low ebb in morale. Yet he gave no thought to quitting. He received a messenger who came from Obregon demanding his surrender, and shot the man in reply. He became moody. He decided he would flee to his old hideout in the Sierra Gamon and start all over.

Late in 1915, therefore, bandit Villa was again a fugitive with scarcely more than the clothes on his back. But an early sense of caution came now to his rescue. When he was riding high he had thoughtfully made a cache of arms and ammunition at several isolated points in the mountains, usualy in caves. These hidden treasures were known to only a few of his men, and most of them had been killed. Now he was able to attract new recruits and outfit them. They stole cattle and raided villages for other provisions, including clothes and—most important of all—girls. It was the old pattern, and it was satisfactory once more.

In due time Pancho decided his new bandit band was strong enough to venture out for larger efforts. He had no hint that the first victim was to cause international headlines. Early in 1916 a passenger train was rolling from Chihuahua City to the mines of Cusihuiriachic. Villa ordered two of his subordinates, Lopez and Castro, to take a group of men and rob the train. These two loyal Villistas were happy to find nineteen Americans among the passengers and, considering the United States now an enemy of Villa, promptly shot eighteen of them. Villa himself deplored the act and said so, nevertheless it was done by his band and he saw indignation leap high in two nations. Carranza issued a decree authorizing any citizen to shoot the outlaw Pancho Villa on sight.

That nineteenth American passenger, the one left unharmed in the butchery, escaped death solely because she was a rather attractive woman. Lopez and Castro reasoned that Villa might want her for a personal prize. Numbed with fear, she made no protest when they put her astride a horse and fled with her back to Villa's hideout. He was happy to welcome her. He reverted to the kittenish antics he sometimes showed in the presence of pretty women.

"*Señorita*," he bowed in exaggerated way. "Is good to have you call on Pancho Villa. You have a name? And why are you traveling on train where bandits can kill you?"

A fair question—Why indeed? Her answer was that she had come to find her husband, one of the army of adventurers whom the decade of excitement had lured into Mexico. She had found no trace of him, felt sure he was dead, and she expected now to die herself.

"Then *I* will be your husband, *señora*," Pancho offered. But when she shook her head in terror, he added, "*Bueno*. You don't want me, I don't want you. I never force myself on women. You will have a ride to safety." She got it.

But *some*body ought to pay for all the Americans' perfidy, Pancho now felt. An American Colonel Tompkins wrote, "When we remember the concessions that Villa gave us when the United States demanded them, we are obliged to confess that he had a right to be angry. He had proven that he, not Carranza, was the one most friendly toward the States. Even in August, 1915, he returned to their owners more than a million dollars in properties taken from American citizens, all on appeal of General Scott." But no such feeling of fairness reached Pancho now.

Betrayal, defeat and rout, personal frustration, all these factors contributed to his new campaign of cruelty against Carranza and against the United States. This campaign reached its climax in an episode that commanded the greatest alarm of all. He learned ultimately that it caused Americans in every city, town, and village to shiver a little in apprehension, then to shake their fists in anger and demand a new revenge of their own. Yet Pancho Villa himself knew he was completely innocent. In fact he was, once more, the victim rather than the aggressor.

Hoping desperately to regain friendship of the United States, he had accepted a secret invitation to visit Washington, D. C., in person and call on the president. A confidential agent of the Associated Press in Los Angeles, California, was the go-between. An Associated Press man, George L. Seese, on February 18, 1916, sent a letter to Villa urging him to accept the preliminary arrangements, then carry out any plans. Villa was to cross the international border quietly at an isolated place just south of Columbus, New Mexico. He was delighted to accept. He moved close to the border with his band of outlaws, traveling by night to avoid the soldiers of Carranza who constantly sought him. His men would wait in the wilderness while he made his trip and returned. He felt sure that he could talk it out with the U. S. president man to man and reestablish good will.

Nearing the border, however, he got word that the plan was called off. The United States had coldly cut off all contact with Villa.

It was a terrific blow. "What can a man do?" he begged of a friend in his headquarters tent that night. "We trust them, and again they turn against us. Yet I think only a few may be to blame. Maybe if I wait here, my friend General Scott can reopen the arrangements for me."

General Scott, unfortunately, was critically embarrassed. "The recognition of Carranza," Scott wrote in his memoirs later, "converted into a bandit the man who had helped us most. We let Carranza send troops through American territory and aided him to crush Villa. I did everything in my power to prevent it. I have never been in such an embarrassing position. Villa, being a simple man, thought I had betrayed him. Never has any man had more right to such belief."

Finding out that the plan of their leader to visit Washington had failed, the indignant followers of Villa decided to take action on their own. They were hungry, half naked, barefoot peons, the same kind of men with whom the young Villa had started his career. They knew nothing of national politics. They knew only that Pancho had been betrayed again and that they feared a firing squad if they didn't starve first. In the beginning, Pancho knew nothing of their desperate thinking.

On the night of March 8, 1916, four hundred of them quietly left camp, rode up the deep ditch that carries flash floods past Columbus, New Mexico, and attacked the town.

In Mexico it would scarcely have made a ripple; towns this size regularly changed hands in military episodes, leaving a toll of dead and wounded. But this was on the sacred soil. And *while Pancho Villa himself quietly nursed his feelings in camp south of the border*, his men gave the United States a dressing down that they felt it so richly deserved.*

19

TEN DAYS passed before Pancho learned what excitement the impulsive raid on Columbus had created. An intimate friend came with newspapers and verbal reports to his hideout in the hills.

"They are sending an *army* after me?" He couldn't believe what the friend said. "Me, with only these little few hungry men left?"

"They are that. An army of 10,000 soldiers."

"Ten thousand! Madre de Dios, *I* have four hundred!"

The friend had a sense of humor. "That about balances, General. It takes 10,000 *gringos* to match four hundred Villistas, sir. They are commanded by a General Juan — Juan —" He paused, studying the odd surname in the newspaper. "Pay—Payrsheeng. Juan Payersheeng. You know of him, General?"

-----

*This matter is no longer controversial. All of Villa's kin and friends, interviewed in the research for this story, insisted that Pancho took no part whatsoever in the famous raid. The American General Scott himself has verified this.—O. A.

"Pershing! Hell's entrails, yes! Shook my hand like a friend. The son of a beech." He added that last in English, as an appropriate afterthought.

"Yes sir."

"I did not expect this. I thought the little group of *gringo* soldiers at Columbus would chase us a few hours, maybe. Now this."

"The whole United States is after your scalp, General. Read it here, sir."

It was true. The Colossus of the North for the first time in its history had been invaded by a foreign "army," Pancho read.

"If necessary we must crush the whole of Mexico to earth in order to avenge this insult to our sovereignty!" the editorial writers in America screamed.

Pancho now regretted very much that he *hadn't* gone on the Columbus raid; he had missed the fun that caused the excitement, though he was being damned for it. He began to pace back and forth, fists doubled, brow furrowed.

"They dare to invade Mexico!" he stormed. "They promise friendship, then they turn against me and send an army. There is not one honest man north of the Rio Grande. They have no right or reason to send 10,000 of their stinking soldiers down here!"

That considered opinion, he learned, was shared by his own enemy at home; President Carranza himself protested vigorously to Washington, saying that it was his Federal government's duty and right to run down Villa, bring him to trial and make reparations. Pancho knew that Carranza might have convinced Wilson in Washington, but neither he nor Wilson could convince the American public. The *gringo* nation already was inflamed by the war in Europe; fearful and jumpy and needful of a whipping boy for its nerves. Pancho realized that he had provided it. In addition, he knew that the calmer *gringo* army leaders saw in their punitive expedition on Mexican soil an excellent training for probable European fighting.

"But this Pershing," grinned Pancho, malevolently now, "he can't catch us even if he brings ten million instead of ten thousand men. He cannot chase an ant with an elephant." Fury still rode Pancho.

The ant in this case ran so fast that Pershing's wagons, men, guns, and materiel became objects of ridicule. They had crossed into Mexico on March 15, just one week after the Columbus raid. Thirty days later they were no nearer to Pancho Villa than they had been at crossing; or if they were, they didn't know it. The highly mobile Pancho, more at home in a saddle than in a bed, often watched them from hiding, laughing at them while he sang "La Cucaracha" with his friends.

> *La Cucaracha, La Cucaracha,*
> *He is a gringo with ten thousand men;*
> *La Cucaracha, La Cucaracha,*
> *His pants are filled from Pancho's dirty wind.*

The Villistas created twenty or so new stanzas expressing their contempt for Pershing and all other Americans. Pancho, head thrown back, chest out, sang loudest of all.

One night in the mountains the Yankees were doing some singing of their own around their camp fires. They had sentries out, as usual, but there had been no military action, and it can be assumed that the sentries were homesick. At any rate it was no problem for Pancho, out of his uniform now and clad as a penniless peon, to take two close friends and creep up within fifty yards of the campfire. They moved as did the Indians of old — a step among the rocks, freeze, a step or two more and freeze again. Thus they fused into the shrubbery, they were just more shadows in the fire-pierced night. A Davy Crockett or a Dan'l Boone might have spotted them, but not these camp-trained soldiers of 1916. Pancho and his friends lay there grinning and unseen for an hour and learned one of the Americans' songs. When they had crept back to their own camp, two miles away in a dark canyon, they began singing—

> *Shee's a long wa-a-a-y to Teepa-raree,*
> *She's a long wa-a-a-ay, to go-o-o—*

He asked one of his better educated Villistas about the song, one who spoke good English. "Thees Teepararee, Benito," he tried it in English himself, "w'at you know about her, eh? You find her for me, maybe?"

"No, no, General. Tipperary is a place, not a girl. It is—"

Big Pancho grabbed the man and shook him in mock anger. "You pool my lag? You make the fon? The music, she say *'She's the sweetes' girl I know.'* Hah! You lie to me!"

Such adventures broke the tedium of being a fugitive. Lay low by day, travel to a new lair by night, wait in the rocks, the canyons, the trees, watch the enemy, damn the *gringos,* laugh at them, stay out of harm's way but scout for something to eat—such was the routine. The distinguished General Pancho Villa, a military genius, big enough to refuse the presidency of a great republic, the man with a mansion and a private train. . . . All that was yesterday, and this was today. But then—one shrugs and philosophizes that this has its compensations; there is hunger and discomfort and danger here, and not a God's sign of a woman to warm one's belly at night, but there are no monumental problems of state, no armies to provision and command, no multitude of intrigues and traitors and opportunists and administrative details. A man *could* sing a little out here in the wilderness hills.

Pancho, then, actually enjoyed flight from the punitive expedition, up to a point. Beyond that, remaining invisible presented its problems. Fearing he might be trapped, and wanting ultimately to carry on his war against Carranza, he threw himself once more into rebuilding his strength. It was not so easy as it had been when an aura of romance and glamor floated around him, yet his name still had magnetic force for the peons. He gathered several hundred of them and outfitted them with arms and clothing from his hidden stores or from stolen goods.

The Americans had divided into three columns seeking him, he learned, and they were aided by Carranza's troops. Most of the time he successfully avoided them, though there were skirmishes involving some of his men. When he felt strong enough, he decided to attack the town of Guerrero. Doing so, he defeated the Carranzistas there and forced them to flee.

Sheer luck then struck him down. He, the matchless cavalryman who had led countless charges against bullets raining like hail, was calmly driving out the few straggling enemies at Guerrero when one of them swung around and fired wildly. The bullet hit Pancho in the leg.

He had never been hurt before, and he couldn't adapt himself. The bullet had fractured a bone and stayed in the flesh. Before a doctor could be found, an Indian sucked the wound and spat out the blood. Because he had to flee after looting the town, the leg became a major problem. An all-night ride in a bouncing car nearly killed him. At dawn the leg had swollen to twice its normal size and he had to be put on a stretcher carried by six men. He was furious, but helpless.

His scouts and spies soon reported that news of the raid brought a rush of Carranzistas and American troops to the area, bent on running him down once and for all. Then he smiled because they could not cope with his early training, he knew more tricks of flight than all their brains could match. Carried into camp at sundown, he would rest himself, eat, then be moved in darkness to an altogether different area for sleep. This old Indian trick precluded any nighttime surprise.

From somewhere—from nowhere known—a young woman materialized in his camp. Doubtless one of his men had been shrewd enough to bring her there, but Pancho first discovered her when he awoke to find her dressing his feverish wound. She spoke little, but her tenderness worked as good a miracle as the few drugs she had. He was kind to her. Mostly she used potassium permanganate solution, and it seemed to work. The swelling subsided, but the leg was terrifically sore. Pancho guided his men to his most secret hideout of all, a place reached by going through half a dozen canyons, over a ridge, down a valley to a cliff edge then climbing to a prehistoric cave. The woman stayed with him.

"Two of you go back and make yourselves known," he ordered. "Say that you were my prisoners but escaped. And tell everybody that Pancho Villa has died of a wound. Understand? I am dead."

It was a good ruse, and it worked. It served to stop pursuit for a while, giving him time to escape. His men tied long ropes to his stretcher, climbed rock walls like flies, and lifted him to the cave. Four men stayed up there with him. The rest of his force, carefully dispersed, stayed miles away at the foot of the sierra, watching for whatever might develop. Thus was the grand general of the revolution holed in, concealed. He knew he was at the lowest ebb of his career since his escape from the Mexico City prison, yet he was oddly content, feeling inner peace. He didn't even suffer his compulsion to over-eat, or to bed down with a girl.

Next day the woman was allowed to climb the cave and again tend him. Few medicines remained now, but she knew a trick or two from peon rearing, Pancho learned. A dog had followed them, encouraged by the men because a dog can be a good sentry, can smell or hear enemies approaching in ambush long before human senses can detect them. The woman asked that the dog be brought into the cave, and again ropes were used.

Three times a day, then, she unbound Pancho's leg and allowed the animal to lick the wound. She had known, as many another earthy person including Pancho had known, that dog saliva seemed to hold some strange curative value for festered sores. She also gathered fresh cactus "ears," sliced them, and made poultices for the wound. Pancho, though approving, nevertheless spent most of his time groaning. Strong individual that he was, possibly the strongest ever turned out by Mexico, he knew he was acting babyish about this wound and its pain, and he didn't care.

"It is the way men are, *señores*," he heard the woman apologize for him, to his friends. "Any woman can stand more pain than any man."

Food was a second major problem. They had come in with a little rice, dried meat or jerky, and water in some jars. The woman made trips down in daytime search for edible roots, cactus fruits, grasshoppers, anything that might help. Such goings and comings were discouraged, for Pancho's sentries knew now that a column of American soldiers had come into the area and were camped less than two miles away. Scouts with field glasses might spot her leaving the cave any day. Yet hunger made them desperate.

One morning she went out with great caution, but never returned. Pancho never knew what happened to her. Possibly she fell and died in a rocky canyon, he reasoned, or was struck by a rattlesnake. She was missed. Pancho had to endure six weeks of hell in the cave. It included times of delirium, times when his own men told him he was insane and he stood up with drawn pistols threatening to kill them for saying so. He had no surcease from these sufferings until enough time passed— Time, the great healer, abetted in this instance by a wandering cow.

The cow must have been one of those bovines that often escape from herds and go wild in the mountains, Pancho decided. His men found her, butchered her, began feeding their leader nourishing beef-blood broth, then meat. In due course he was a strong man again, but realized that he had an almost negligible "army" now.

The last stages of his convalescence had given him time to do much thinking and planning. His under-cover agents, of whom he had many from eager volunteers, brought word that the Americans had passed on, looking for him elsewhere. So, once more he set out to recruit a "ghost army," one known to exist and be strong yet almost never visible. It mushroomed like fighting clans of old, by word of mouth, by whispers in cantinas, by gravel against windows at night, by secret signs and blood pledges under the stars.

"Villa is down but never out," he himself told adoring peons, as opportunity arose. "I have had to hide, but you have shown great loyalty and faith in me. Now I call on you once more to fight with me for Mexico's freedom."

He backed that patriotic appeal with a promise of food and clothing—which he knew was a good thing for any recruiter to do. And he got his men. Soon he was the untamed rebel again. News of his "death" had been accepted on several occasions as gospel—there had even been a photographed grave and a cross bearing Pancho's name, carefully planted there by his men. Pancho laughed big, reading the paper. But when the grave was opened by Federalistas wanting to exhibit his body as a prize, they found only the stripped bones of that cow.

Meanwhile, his colleague in fighting Carranza, General Emiliano Zapata, had continued his part of the rebellion in the southern states of Mexico, where his followers alternately worked in the fields and fought their battles. Villa took heart from that and resolved to gain back the northern half of the country.

His first real test of new strength came at the retaking of his home town, Chihuahua City. Knowing the value of audacity, he announced a few days in advance that he would celebrate Mexico's Independence Day, the 16th of September when all the nation normally enjoyed fiesta, in Chihuahua City's beautiful squares.

He did just that. Quietly he used an infiltration technique this time, sending some hundred of his men into the town in twos and three, guns hidden under loose peon garments or concealed in loads of hay or in straw, rugs, anything· available. By agreement, these men started shooting at 3 a.m. wherever they were.

178

The quick confusion worked just as Pancho had planned. It gave him and his main force opportunity to dash in. He took the strong Penitentiary, serving now as fortress, with only three hundred Dorados. Though the defending Carranzistas numbered over 3,000, they became so confused that they started shooting one another. When the inevitable "VIVA VILLA" was heard, Pancho gleefully saw hundreds of Carranza's men promptly desert to his own side. Two hundred prisoners, freed from the Penitentiary-fortress, took up arms with Villa at once.

Before 9 a.m. on the big holiday, then, Pancho was addressing the happily conquered populace from the balcony of the governor's palace. Then he took sixteen truck loads of ammunition, guns, and food, besides many horses and much other loot, and quietly departed, pausing for only a few other essential things.

"Señor," he said to the town's chief of police, "please do not let it be said that Pancho Villa ever was a kidnaper of women. Note that I have in my car here two beautiful girls. Many have come to see me this morning, offering their congratulations and themselves. Will you now ask these two if they accompany me of their own free will? If they say no, you shall escort them back to their families."

He smiled as the girls scorned the chief's offer of "rescue." They had indeed come voluntarily, and enthusiastically, and if they knew nothing of Pancho's past adventures in love, they cared less. Later Pancho knew, unfortunately, that he himself made one mistake here. In his gratitude, or whatever it was he felt, he took one of the girls to the ancient and beautiful cathedral that very hour, cornered a frightened young padre, stuck a pistol in his ribs and commanded a marriage ceremony as he had done before. When it was performed, he took his new wife back to the car—and the other girl promptly attacked her!

The fight was notable. It attracted a crowd of spectators. Pancho, quite helpless here, had no recourse; he had to lift his spare, his reserve wife-to-be, right out of the car and go off without her, beautiful though she was.

He could not linger in Chihuahua City, he explained to news men, because Pershing's men would rush there to capture him. He had no choice during this period except to hit and run. This he did again and again, with consummate skill.

He marched from victory to victory throughout the state of

179

Chihuahua, establishing a new prestige for himself there and making both Pershing and Carranza look foolish. He even sped back to Chihuahua City on November 27 and captured it again! He laid traps for his pursuers, and laughed when they were caught. Once, like some storied Joaquin Murietta in California's pioneer days, he found a sign offering a reward for his capture, took the sign off its post and, grinning big, boldly rode into an enemy major's headquarters with it. He pretended to be bearing a message for the major.

"*Señores*," he greeted the major, after confronting that man and his five aides inside, "I have here a photo of myself. I came to get the reward money. You don't believe it is me? Look!"

He saw them look. First at the picture, then at him. As they looked, the light of terror showed in their eyes. He made it wholly justified. In a lightning-like flash of action the two pistols of Pancho Pistolas were out and flaming. The six men fell in their tracks. Only one of them had managed to draw his own gun and fire. Two guards rushed in and were clubbed insensible.

By the time more help could arrive, Pancho was on the Major's own horse—it was finer than the one he had ridden, and had a saddle with much hand tooled silver. He leaned low and was gone before any thought of pursuit could be organized.

He explained that he did such things not merely in a spirit of personal adventure, but for their very real effect on other men, enemies as well as his own followers. He was consciously rebuilding the Villa legend. At this stage he sensed that his shrewdness, his daring, his all around skill, seemed to have matured. His pitiful little barefoot band that clung loyally to him while hiding in the Sierra, had metamorphosed into a powerful army again. He had nearly 3,000 soldiers, reasonably well trained, when he went to claim that reward. Soon they numbered nearly 6,000 and his under officers were working them dawn to dusk, conditioning them and instilling discipline.

This force of course inevitably had to do battle. It was not always victorious, but it was a threat at every stage. With it Pancho gave no peace to the dictator in Mexico City and no peace of mind to the president in Washington. President Wilson was not sleeping well anyway, Pancho learned; a foreign dictator, one named Wilhelm in Germany, was keeping half the world awake nights. Pancho Villa saw Woodrow Wilson have to eat the proud proclamation that "We are too proud to fight." That fact, plus Villa's elusiveness and mounting strength despite all the efforts to capture him, forced an unforgettable American retreat in January of 1917. Mr. Wilson ordered his punitive expedition to Mexico withdrawn.

"La Cucaracha, La Cucaracha,

sang the exuberant Villistas, plus many thousands of other Mexicans now happy to sing with them—

"He sent a boy to catch a famous man;
La Cucaracha, La Cucaracha,
The boy caught nothing but a dose of fan."

"Fan," Pancho knew, was an American word made into Mexican idiom meaning, sadly enough, syphilis.

Unwary U. S. soldiers, exposed for the first time to Mexico's famous romantic charms, had not known how to be selective; they had fallen victims of *cantina señoritas* boldly flickering their pretty eyelashes behind pretty fans. Their subsequent ill health became widely known, just as their failure to catch Pancho was to make them a laughingstock in Mexico for the ensuing fifty years.

Pancho himself paid little attention to Pershing's withdrawal, except to laugh at it. He was too busy. It developed late in 1917 that he had overstretched himself again; some embarrassing defeats accrued for his army. These were due almost invariably to a shortage of ammunition. In one instance his ferocious Dorados charged into the thickest part of a battle with no ammunition whatsoever, fighting only with rifle butts, bayonets and swords. For two years Villa kept every possible agent busy trying to smuggle arms to him, but the enemy forces knew his need and cut him off time and time again. Moreover, treasonable "friends" arose anew to plague him; some of the ones he trusted most sold his plans to the enemy, forcing a last minute change. It was enough to dishearten any leader. It served only to make Pancho Villa more determined than ever; it built in him a magnificent anger.

To top off Pancho's troubles, Carranza hired an assassin for $50,000 to murder the rebel forces' other dedicated general, the one waging war on the dictator in the southern half of Mexico. Emiliano Zapata thus was slain on April 10, 1919, leaving Villa

181

as the sole important champion of the people's cause.

He was a tired champion. He had the willingness, the persistence, the courage, he even had enough loyal men to fight with him. He could not outfit them. There were times when he cried tears of anger at this frustration. Then rather than just cry and berate the two enemies, Carranza and Wilson, he decided on a course of action which he knew was pure storybook, one of those plans that could have taken substance only in some highly romantic nation and personality. In fiction, it would have been overdrawn, far fetched. In fact, it was delightful melodrama, one of the high points in Pancho's colorful career.

"The time has come," he confided to a close friend, "for Carranza himself to die. We cannot capture him with our armies because we lack ammunition and supplies. So, some patriot must go right up to him and shoot him down."

"You would not stoop to hiring an assassin, General Villa, as he did for Zapata?" The friend was appalled.

"*Madre de Dios*, no! I am no murderer!" That could have been a moot point, but no issue of it was made now.

"Then who will kill him?"

"I will. I, Pancho Villa."

He meant just what he said. He ordered his army to divide into groups, retire to the regions whence they had come, and await his call about three months later. Then he with fifty picked companions went under cover, disguising themselves as Robin Hood's men might have done, and headed for Mexico City. As they neared the city, they began displaying a black banner embroidered with a white skull—Carranza's own flag in Chihuahua. They posed as Carranza soldiers on a mission to buy horses. They hoped to infiltrate the big city, study the dictator-president's movements, and so set up a time and place for Pancho to make the kill.

Pancho, elated, felt that it was a fine plot worthy of him or any other heroic man of action in either fact or fiction. He was crushed when it failed. He thought maybe a traitor tipped off the enemy, or some glowering henchman of the dictator just got suspicious of the "horse buyers." At any rate he and his men were suddenly trapped one day when they stopped for food in the town of Juejuquillo. Villa had to grab the mayor of the town and hold him as a hostage at pistol point, while the conspirators backed away. He knew they were lucky to get out alive.

Later he sent five of his trusted fifty into Mexico City to do the scouting for him. They were to report in secret, and he was to creep into the city disguised as a peon peddler—with a high powered rifle concealed in baskets that he carried. It could have slain Carranza at long range.

Again fate intervened. The five spies never returned to him, and he finally decided that they too were trapped, then killed.

An alarm was sounded for Villa, saying that he was reported somewhere in the region of the capital. He heard about it almost every hour. He had no hope of success now. He had no choice but to slip up the hedgerows and the arroyos by night, fighting starvation and danger while he worked back to the northward where he might again contact his main body of men.

20

PANCHO now rediscovered that Failure had its rewards just as Success exacts its price. If he had killed Carranza as planned, he would have felt temporary exultation, then would have eaten too much, become sick to his stomach, and suffered depression. He knew that, and was comforted because he had no such reaction now.

Thus he remained calm for the ensuing weeks and was able to do his best thinking while also enjoying a badly needed rest. He let the weeks stretch into months, doing little with his shattered "army" except make a few guerrilla thrusts.

One stroke of fortune came from outside, he discovered. Many Mexicans had been forced into exile by the Carranza pressures. These lived in the American border towns and some in New York City, so they got together and formed an organization to encourage the Revolutionary cause at home. Through them Pancho was able to obtain much help. He was their chief hope, he realized. Among the big events in his favor was their enabling General Felipe Angeles to return to him. Felipe traveled in secret, and when he finally came to Villa the two old friends rushed to one another's arms. They talked like long-separated brothers for more than two hours. At the end, Pancho asked Felipe to take charge of conditioning and training his troops.

"Very well," said Felipe. "I start at once. Come with me, Pancho."

They walked out after all the Villistas, about seven hundred at the moment, were ordered onto the drill fields without arms. Felipe told them they were to practice running the fifty-yard dash today, and longer runs each day thereafter. The sergeants took charge and the track work began. Felipe turned to his friend.

"Now Pancho," said he, "*you* run."

His commander looked at him, astonished. "Me?"

"Yes, you. Hell's bells, look at your belly! Are you a sow about to be delivered of fourteen pigs?"

Pancho studied his figure. It was indeed massive, and a great deal of it was superfluous. He had already known it; he had even planned—as all fattening people plan—to do something about it immediately, perhaps even tomorrow.

"You have been shoveling in too many tamales and enchiladas, my corpulent friend," Felipe went on. "The grease of the revolution makes you too big for your belt. I should never have left you alone so long. Have you had several expert female cooks?"

"I have had nothing to do with women." Pancho was embarrassed.

"Ha! *That* would be something now. Let me tell you, if you did lure a pretty girl to your bed, with you shaped like a pregnant pigeon—Pancho damn it, get on the mark, right there. When I say 'GO,' you start running. I'm going to have you doing the hundred yards in ten seconds before I let you eat again."

Never in all his long life of adventure—Pancho swore it—had he suffered so. He tried pleading. He tried getting mad and roaring. On the fourth day he threatened with his two pistols drawn to shoot Felipe Angeles to death.

Felipe calmly walked right up to the muzzles of the guns and took them from Pancho's hands. "You are acting childish. Now get out there and run. You'll dog-trot half a mile this morning and another half this afternoon. And I'm supervising your chow."

Thus Felipe rebuilt Pancho's strength. The process strengthened their friendship, too. One day after six weeks of it, Pancho offered

184

a prize of a hundred pesos in gold for the best hand-wrestler in his command—and won it himself, though at least nine strong fellows tried their best. He gave each of them a hundred pesos.

Soon the up-and-down General Francisco Villa found his fortune sufficiently up again to go on the warpath in another headline-making campaign. He operated as before in Chihuahua —"I was born in Durango but the state of Chihuahua is my home," said he in a speech to his troops. "The very rocks know me here."

His new army and Dorados included many old followers plus many eager young recruits who were awed by the name of Villa. He made a point of greeting the new ones personally, shaking their hands, asking of their home life. Most were peons as he had been. He learned from one that a wife and five near-naked kids had been left behind.

"Take this money and buy food and clothing for them," Pancho ordered. "Go back to your village and take care of your family."

The young man pleaded for permission to stay.

"Very well," said his commander. "Is there an old man you trust? Go home, hire him to work your little farm and look after your people. Say to him that Pancho Villa will personally cut his guts if he tries to sleep with your wife. Get food and shoes for them. Then you hurry back here to fight with me."

The young fellow came back bringing sixteen recruits; men couldn't resist the magic of Pancho Villa.

Thus enthusiasm swelled again like that of a college cheering section, and the "team" was as desperately eager to fight. With them Pancho swept through many of his old haunts, recapturing such important citadels as Parral, Chihuahua City, and Juarez. He had to take Juarez twice, because some of his men began looting too soon after the first easy victory, were driven out, then driven back by Pancho himself. Again he saw that it all had some comic-opera aspects, except that blood and suffering are never comic.

At Juarez he had a clash with the neighbors once more. Some of his bullets inevitably crossed the Rio Grande into El Paso. Fort Bliss, nearby, responded with cannon shots. No great damage was done either way, but Pancho's hatred of Americans was intensified.

His unhappiness grew worse when a traitor named Salas

collected a reward of 15,000 pesos for betraying Felipe Angeles. The Carranza forces gave him a mock trial and executed him on November 26, 1919. Facing death, Felipe made the most stirring plea for freedom ever heard in Mexico. To save his own skin, Villa was forced to flee with his small army into the mountains.

At Felipe's death Pancho cried like a child, then remained completely silent for five days. He knew he had lost not only his closest friend, but the one man who might have "thought him through" to ultimate victory. In this moment of despair, Pancho began to realize that his star was on the decline.

"I am mightily tired," he confessed to another friend a week or so after Felipe was buried.

He sensed that it was spiritual fatigue, actually; an emotional exhaustion. He realized that no man could live the life he had known for twenty-five years and not be worn thin.

He had more and more trouble getting equipment for his men. A few years before, he could lead a hundred followers into a ranch and confiscate enough horses to mount all his cavalry. Now the ranches of Chihuahua were stripped bare, many of them turned back to wilderness with only a few wild cattle to be found in the thickets and hills, most of the buildings burned. In short, he discovered that the revolution was as exhausted as its leader.

When he dispersed his troops temporarily for safety, to avoid capture, and waited quietly in the vicinity of Pilar de Conchos, a committee of women asked to see him. As always, he bade them welcome.

"General Villa," their spokesman said, "we beg of you to come to the cathedral for the christening of our children. We want you to be their godfather."

"Me? Me, of all people?" He was sincere in his modesty. "Once I was powerful, my friends. Now I am nothing. Your babies should have godfathers who can serve them."

"We want no one else, General. Their fathers were members of your army. If you christen them, they too can grow up to fight for your cause. God will guide them toward it."

He had expected a dozen, maybe twenty, at the christening ceremonies. More than one hundred and fity appeared, peon mothers each with a child of the sun on her hip, brown little bits of humanity who held in their embryonic minds the future of

186

Mexico. Pancho was touched, even tearful. He kissed each of them, managed to find for each a gift. For the Camargo priest who conducted the baptisms, he had three hundred silver pesos.

"What of your own soul, my son?" the good padre asked, before parting. "Is the famous Pancho Villa allied with God?"

This was a sad and drama-charged moment there in the cathedral of Conchos. A warrior such as he cannot have a soul, he told himself, for how could it live? A human soul feeds on good deeds. He felt the seed of his peon mother stirring in him, but the thousands he had slain swam through his consciousness, the vision of women ravaged haunted him. The mood did not last long. Pancho Villa was no dying old man reliving his life. He walked out of the church with his head erect, his jaw clamped tight.

When he could resume the guerrilla fighting he ran smack into another "enemy" of which he knew virtually nothing. He had led some five hundred of his men against a small town, had captured and looted it, was happily fleeing back to the hills next day when he heard a strange sound break the sanctity of the Mexican sky.

The source of it looked as strange as the sound itself. He saw many of his Indian peon Villistas frankly cry out in terror, while most of the others knelt, crossed themselves, and began muttering. He himself was greatly alarmed.

Because a Thing, a mechanical bird, a noisy creation with weird wings had topped a little rise, swooped on them and dropped a bomb! Pancho was appalled.

The bomb missed the riders by four hundred yards, but its effect on morale was devastating. General Villa recognized the Thing at once. Felipe Angeles had told him about it, saying it was used extensively by the *gringos* and Germans in the World War. He had to make quite a speech about this flying machine to his ignorant though loyal followers, assuring them he would cope with it. But he had been thoroughly frightened.

"The worst fact," said he to his staff that evening, "is that they can follow us when we flee. They can easily see us and send the enemy right where we are."

Thus the airplane had the same impact that the machine gun had had earlier. It spelled defeat. He could not get planes, but the Carranza forces could.

He did quickly learn to travel by night and employ camouflage by day, so that the planes' scouting abilities were lost. The planes had limited range, and once he was in the Sierra he could outwit any pilot. But there the flying enemy was, if the Villistas came out; a dangerous potential; one more heavy straw on his back.

It was heavier, he soon realized, than the new reward now offered throughout Mexico for the head of Pancho Villa. Deliver that head, on its body alive or not, and collect 100,000 pesos. So said the Carranza government.

Next good news he had was that Carranza himself had lost his head. The fierce old dictator had many enemies, Pancho knew. Unlike Villa, some of these aspired to his job. One was named Obregon. With great cleverness Obregon trapped Carranza, forced him to flee from the capital city toward Vera Cruz. But his trains were caught and he was captured. Then in the dawn of May 21, 1920, in a cabin at Tlaxcaltongo, an assassin killed him. Pancho was delighted, although some fighting still lay ahead of him. He wished he could avoid it, but he knew he was technically an "outlaw" even with Carranza gone. When Congress designated Adolfo de la Huerta as temporary president, Pancho Villa was willing to make some compromises. To have fought this new de la Huerta would have meant an entirely new "revolution," and Mexico, he knew, had already suffered a tragic plague of them. The basic ideal would be lost in any prolongation of welfare, Pancho now felt. He let his attitude be known.

Therefore when Villa in the town of Parral placed a telephone call direct to the office of President de la Huerta in Mexico City, it was received.

"I have no desire to keep on fighting the government of my people," General Villa stated after proper identification. "If you, Mr. President, will give me your personal and public guarantee to help instill my ideals, then we can be friends."

"I feel that our ideals are the same, General Villa. It shall be done. I give you here and now my promise. You want freedom for the poor people, the peons. So do I. You want to end the favoritism showed popular ranchers and politicians. So do I. You want to stop oppressions by the dictatorial members even of the clergy. So do I."

"Then we can reach an agreement, sir. I put my trust in you."

The telephone conference lasted nearly an hour. The president promised to send his emissary, General Eugenio Martinez, to meet Pancho in person and work out final details.

As he left the telephone, Pancho saw his staff and aides watching him intently. They knew something big was in the air, he realized, for they saw tears in his eyes, and he didn't mind. The tired but still fierce rebel, a man of great emotional intensity anyway, paused before them and made his pronouncement: "At last I have found a man who really understands me. My revolutionary career is over. I am about to become a farmer!"

Not long afterward, a formal pact was signed. Pancho was almost boyishly interested in the procedure. He had never felt the need for much office routine, knew little of flowery governmental phrases. But with only a little help from friends, he was able to read and understand this important pact:

> In the city of Sabinas, Coahuila, at 11 a.m. on the 28th day of July, 1920, we the undersigned, Generals Francisco Villa and Eugenio Martinez, make known and certify: That after thorough discussions to consolidate peace in the Mexican Republic, we have reached a cordial and satisfactory agreement, the first party accepting, in his name and that of his army, the stipulations proposed by the Executive Power through the second party which are the following:
>
> *FIRST*. General Villa gives up arms to retire to private life.
>
> *SECOND*. The Executive Power will give, as his property, and by legal means, to General Villa, the Hacienda de Cañutillo in the state of Durango, the ownership title to belong to him. Villa must retire to this Hacienda general.
>
> *THIRD*. In the above mentioned place, General Villa will have an escort formed by fifty men in his confidence, who he himself will designate and who be approved by the Department of War and Navy which will pay their salaries. Such an escort cannot be removed nor diverted from its only subject, which is to take care of the personal security of the aforementioned General.
>
> *FOURTH*. The rest of the persons who actually form part of General Villa's forces, including those presently in this city as well as those who are in other parts of the Republic performing commissions ordered by General Villa, will receive from the government a year's salary, according to

their present rank. In addition, they will be donated lands for their ownership, in the places where they wish to work them.

FIFTH. The persons who desire to stay in the Army will be incorporated into the National Army.

General Villa promises, on his word of honor, not to rise in arms against the constituted government, nor against his fellow citizens. On his part, General Martinez promises in the same manner to loyally see that the aforementioned conditions are respected and that General Villa and the persons who have formed his army have effective guarantees.

As a guarantee, this deed is written and signed by both parties in acceptance, so that the fulfillment of this Pact be kept.

NOTE. The Generals, Commanders, officers and soldiers commanded by General Francisco Villa, are as follows:

One Division General, one Brigade General, 7 Brigadier Generals, 23 Colonels, 25 Lieutenant Colonels, 33 Majors, 52 First Captains, 33 Second Captains, 34 Lieutenants, 41 Second Lieutenants, 31 First Sergeants, 33 Second Sergeants, 14 Corporals and 480 soldiers.

SIGNED: DIVISION GENERAL Eugenio Martinez.
DIVISION GENERAL Francisco Villa.

Thus General Francisco Villa *had not surrendered.*

That fact struck his consciousness immediately, and elated him.

"I have not surrender!" he almost shouted at the American news men present. "You onderstan', *amigos?*"

They nodded, smiling appreciatively.

"I have been defeat many tam in battles, but I have never surrender. Is good."

One reporter spoke up. "And history will know that it was you, sir, who approached the new government, *offering* a truce, not asking for one."

Pancho beamed. "Hah! *Seguro si! Esta bueno!*" He felt high.

"But they are as happy to sign as you are, General. Perhaps happier. They know you are still the most dangerous man in Mexico, the most powerful."

Pancho nodded his appreciation, but added, "I don' want to be danger. I want to be farmer, where I estarted in lifes. Only batter—*¿Sabe ustedes, amigos?* I will make nobody my eslaves, I will rob nobody."

"Sir, it is significant that you have never really been a thief," one reporter spoke up, in a summary that Pancho was always to remember. "Millions of pesos passed through your hands during your career as a revolutionist, but *you never kept one for yourself.* That alone makes you a standout in history."

Pancho again was touched. He remained quiet a long moment, than slowly nodded. "I put him all into the Cause, *amigos,*" he spoke low tone, humbly. "What a man esteal money for himself, eh? Is no good. He go to hell. My mawther, long ago she tell me —" He stopped. He couldn't trust his voice to go on.

Reporters were scribbling fast, he noted. He wasn't much interested, he really didn't care what they wrote and printed about him any more. Once, he knew, his vanity alone would have made him follow up on their work. Now he was indifferent.

"De la Huerta's government has allocated 1,000,000 pesos for you, General Villa," said a reporter, "for you to start developing your agricultural enterprise — right sir? At the Cañutillo Hacienda?"

Pancho nodded. "Is good. I will not waste him. I do my bes'."

A few hours later he was approached by the General Martinez who had signed their compact. Martinez proposed that Villa with his men travel to their new homes in the State of Durango in special trains which the government would provide. Touched anew by this courtesy, Pancho accepted, and reported it to his men.

They would have none of it, he quickly learned. They were not "train riders," they told their General; they were horse riders and infantrymen, they had a pride of their own, they wanted to *march* with Francisco Villa one last time.

Once again, therefore, Pancho Villa's emotions almost got the better of him. He knew he had been paid high tribute, and could not refuse. Even Martinez agreed with him, and Pancho saw that man's deep emotional reactions, too. They solemnly shook hands.

"You are much loved, General," Martinez murmured, and Pancho agreed.

So it was then that General Francisco Villa — "Pancho" now as never before — mounted a big white horse provided for him, squared his shoulders, adjusted the fine gold-braided sombrero that was also a gift, rested the knuckles of his right hand on his hip and yelled the Spanish version of "Forwar-r-r-rd, ho-o-o-o!"

His stallion shook the reins and reared just once. He saw that it was almost like a prearranged signal, because every spectator broke into cheering. Pancho lifted his hand and marched away at the head of his forces for the last time.

Behind him as they started, one happy Dorado broke out with a loud baritone —

"EE-YAH-HA-A-A-A-HAH-HAH-HAH-HAH-A-A-A-A!"
Viva Villa!
Viva Pancho!
Viva La Cucaracha!
La Cucaracha, La Cucaracha,
He is a man to follow all the day;
La Cucaracha, La Cucaracha,
The war is over, now it's time to play!

The old war song swept through the column, so that presently Pancho heard a dozen or more different stanzas. His men made up new words and some of these were lurid indeed, but everywhere there was the fiesta spirit. Pancho sang with them, turning in his saddle, waving his right arm while the left controlled the prancing stallion. He who could shed tears quickly, could just as quickly rise to happy thoughts.

He discovered, with reverent tears, that his reception at every crossroad, village, and town was one for a hero. At Cuatro Cienegas he found the city officials dressed in their best, leading the populace out to greet him with flag waving and cheering. He paused to speak emotionally in an extraordinary session at city hall. Nobody seemed to remember, or care, that Cuatro Cienegas was the birthplace not of Pancho Villa but of the late Venustiano Carranza.

When the picturesque column arrived at San Pedro de las Colonias, Pancho received letters from President de la Huerta, from Secretary of War Calles, and from General Benjamin C. Hill, confirming the pact of peace with its gift of the Hacienda Canutillo, and congratulating him for being the brave patriot that he was.

The triumphal march continued all the long way to Tlahualillo, near Torreon. There he got his men to accept urgent invitations to ride by rail "at least part of the way, to show us you are also

friends of the industrial workers as well as of the farm peons."
They left the train at Parral and continued by land across the
wildly beautiful ranch country to his new Hacienda.

Bold is the warrior, high is the flag. So sang the people in their
many versions of welcome. He had planned to make himself
known as *Señor* — as Mister Francisco Villa. He might have
known better, a reporter told him, smiling. Not in Mexico can
you do that, any more than in America; he would be a General
forevermore even though he never touched arms again.

Along the route of travel, groups of old Villistas had joined
the cavalcade, tearfully happy at what they considered his triumph. Thousands wanted to shake his hand, and he welcomed
all. Every man who had ever ridden with him and came close
now, was given a year's pay before being sent back to his family.

Hundreds, finally thousands, of babies were brought to him;
to be kissed, to be blest as if he were a priest, to be photographed
with him, or just to be touched by him so that proud parents
could tell of it in later years.

"This one looks like me, eh *madrecita?*" he said to several
young mothers, flashing his big infectious grin. "Maybe it *is*
mine, *señora!* Hah! I have made love to you some time maybe?
You remember?"

It was a joke and they all knew it and laughed uproariously, he
loudest of all. Truth is, some of them *were* his get, both he and
the mothers knew. It only added to their prestige and pride.

"Yes, I expect to retire forever and be a farmer," he had to re-
peat again and again to reporters, especially to Americans. His
hatred for *gringos* had softened, and he bade the courteous ones
welcome.

"Will you raise crops and cattle both, General Villa?"

"Yes. But mostly I will try to improve methods, and from what
I learn, will teach my compatriots."

Each such statement made a new headline, he discovered; the
big man, turning his sword into a plowshare.

"Will you personally till the soil, sir?" they would ask.

"If I wish to. But my friends, if I am to be a leader I must
spend much time directing others, eh? I want to test new ma-
chinery. Trucks, and cultivators, and the new farm horse you call
a tractor."

Most of the time he spoke Spanish and let them worry about

the translation. But the meanings became clear. Pancho Villa was to be a country squire, thereby realizing a cherished ambition. Having raided and destroyed many rich ranches in the past twenty years, he was now to be a rich rancher himself.

"But *my* workers will be free, gentlemen," he'd insist always. "They shall be paid well, and live in decency and self respect, with no beatings and meanness. They shall have the security that all of us need."

"And for yourself, sir?"

"For myself?" He'd pause at this one, musing, thinking ahead, savoring his dream, relishing its nearness at last. "For myself I want only what every man wants in his heart — contentment with those he loves. I want most of all — may it please God — to have a regular breakfast, and dinner, and a supper, and a clean soft bed, all in the company of a wife and some happy children. And not have to shoot men or fear them for traitors; or to worry about things bigger than a lame horse or a child's toothache or the need for rain.

"Gentlemen, I want for myself only to be an average man, at home."

21

AT EXACTLY 6 o'clock on this Sabbath morning in 1920 Pancho Villa heard the tower bell on Hacienda Cañutillo break the dawn stillness — "*Bong! Bong-bong! . . . Bong! Bong-bong!*" — repeated until no living soul within half a mile could have remained sleeping.

Pancho himself threw open the front door of the main house when he heard that signal. He had arisen early, a habit dating back to childhood. Now he stepped outside, lifted his head and studied the sky. This too was characteristic as he well knew, smiling at himself. For one whose life is a continual fight, the sky is important, eh? Will the day bring rain, snow, wind, hail? Will it smile beneficently as the Holy Mother might do or will it hold gray threats of disaster? Pancho, arms akimbo, turned completely around, looking afar, sensing inner calm. No matter what the sky held *now*, he told himself, it would be acceptable. Let it rain, indeed! For this day he would command no troops, this day he would lead no cavalry charge. The "Bong!" of the bell he had ordered erected was not a call to arms. It was a lyrical proclamation that a New Day was dawning for Pancho Villa, a day of peace.

He quickly realized that this was understood by the entire Villa family, the cowboys, field workers, blacksmiths, mechanics, the house servants, seamstresses and cooks, all whose livelihood and hopes centered here. Because, even as he stepped out under the sky, every door in sight seemed to open and many a window shutter was flying wide. Men, women and children appeared and they too studied the sky, because the General did so. Hearty greetings were spoken, and behind him he heard the running of children.

"Papa!" one child shrieked, bursting out the door in glee.

Papa Pancho stooped to grab a little girl under her arms then swing her around and around before he lifted her to his great shoulder.

"My Celia!" said he, patting her knee with one hand, making a foot stirrup with the other. "You are ready to eat, eh? You are ready for breakfast?"

Next moment he found a noisy avalanche upon him — Augustin, Octavio, Francisco, Juana Maria, Micaela. Six children can seem like sixty. Papa Pancho squatted on his heels to hug them, to reach out and tousle heads. Then he led all six back inside the entryway, down the corridor and into the big dining room. There the mother (and stepmother) was waiting.

There too, he found four grown men, the Francisco Villa "staff" or what remained of it. They were not a military staff now, but an agrarian one. He had told them they were to be concerned not with deploying troops, stationing cannon, concealing cavalry, intrenching infantry, but with breeding cattle, planting corn, beans, hay, vegetables, fruits, cultivating and harvesting and building a wholly new life for the centaur of the north.

Yet he himself still wore campaign dress, including the belted coat in which he had so often been photographed. He had always liked that coat. Diagonally across his great chest this morning were the cartridge belts that had become a part of his uniform.

195

Two pistols, their silver gleaming, hung at his sides. But without comment he sat down at the head of the long table, and all united in obvious enjoyment of the food. When the eating was done, he arose and smiled happily at them.

"Now!" he exclaimed. "Now is the moment!"

He strode away, leading family and staff to the luxurious living room of the home. With no ceremony, but with directness and simplicity that were even more impressive, he unbuckled the cartridge belts and hung them on pegs above the living room fireplace.

Nobody spoke. He noticed that even the children seemed to sense his earnestness, for they stared at him, waiting. He unbuckled the right hand holster, removed a beautiful shining gun and unloaded it. The cartridges he put carelessly on the mantle, then he laid the pistol there.*

"Pancho Villa himself has just done what no other man has ever been able to do," said he. "Disarm Pancho Villa. I say to you now, my friends, my beloved ones, never again will I take up arms in war. I came from the land, I have loved the land, I am back on the land and here I shall stay. You must help me. Together we must make this a good something. Every morning at six the bell must call us to breakfast, then our work and our day's happiness shall begin."

He saw that most of the home personnel was in the big living room or straining to peer in through the wide doorways. Most of the women present, and some of the men, quietly crossed themselves, and not a few were whispering prayers, he noted with pleasure.

The serious moment ended, General Villa's face broke into the broadest of smiles, his fine teeth gleaming. He suddenly flexed his arm muscles like a wrestler, clapped his huge hands and rubbed their palms together.

"And so it is work for us!" he exclaimed, with great heartiness. "I have chosen you well. You are my loyal ones, you are

---

*This was the last time he ever touched the pistol. Thirty years later in the Villa mansion on Tenth Street in Chihuahua City, Chih., one of Pancho's wives exhibited that same beautiful gun. It had never been reloaded. His jacket, hat, cap and many other possessions were shown.

capable. Let each do his task, and let hatreds die. I have pledged my word to the government and had its word in turn. You have pledged your word to me. Today is a Sunday, so take your ease. But tomorrow at sunrise — ho!"

He felt wonderful, released, free, young again. He invited the children to come with him now, and was gratified when Augustin, Octavio, Pancho, Jr., Juana Marie, Micaela and Celia became his small but delighted army. Striding fast, he looked back at them. *¡Maravilloso!* Much better than leading dirty death-minded men with guns, *no es verdad?* Again he smiled to himself in high gratification.

He knew that the children were the spawn of several wombs, but their maternal origins concerned him not at all. He had at least created a place where he could be at ease and where children — any children — could be loved and feel secure. This was priceless, as he well knew. Austreberta, his current wife and mother of Hipolito yet to be born, he regarded as a good mother, also as an acceptable companion for himself. He gave thought to these homely domestic things as he led his juvenile Dorados on a Sunday morning hike.

On the second Sunday morning, a week later, it occurred to *Señor* Villa that each of his children must have a weekly allowance. He had heard that this was an American custom, and he thought it a good one. So he called out loudly — "HOLA! Children, come here!"

He beamed as they came running. Papa Pancho spelled excitement, always. "Form a circle," he ordered, "back to back. *No* Juana, your back side must be in; everybody back to back, and holding hands. Close your eyes. Tight! One moment — when you hear coins falling, everybody open eyes, turn and grab!"

This was in the patio with a flagstone floor, near the fountain. Quickly he lifted both hands full of coins from his pockets and showered them over the excited children.

"Now!" he signalled.

The scramble was furious. Shrieking boys and girls dived for money everywhere. In the cracks of the flagstones, under the tufts of grass that grew there, around the patio posts — treasure had rolled all over. General Villa was dancing happily, laughing and enjoying the scene so much that Mother Austreberta and some of the servents came to look on.

Presently the noice subsided and he began to check results. Most of the children had fared reasonably well, their hands bulging. One, a girl, held a single coin. It was the penny of Mexico, the *centavo*, almost the size of the American half dollar but of almost negligible purchasing value. She beheld the loot in the others' hands, then looked back at her lone penny. Her eyes turned up to Papa Pancho and she burst into tears.

"Celia, baby!"

He lifted her to his chest, reached for more coins and filled her hands, not with copper coins but with silver. The loot she thus acquired quadrupled that of her brothers and sisters. It was highly satisfying.*

Soon after the youngsters scattered to put their allowances away, one of them, Octavio, came running back through the patio, and stood there watching his father. Pancho spoke to him. "What will you do with your money, son? You will buy something, eh?"

Octavio paused to consider. His pleasure was apparent to father, but so was his indecision. "I could wish for a horse," said he, at last. "My own horse."

"The ranch, so, it has many horses. You may have one. Any one."

"Then a bridle. A bridle of red leather, yes! With ornaments. With silver conchos on the side, papa. May I? Will there be money enough? I could work. And save. Could I have a bridle with silver rosettes, papa? With conchos?"

General Francisco Villa, retired, did not answer him. The huge man just straightened up and his eyes seemed to turn far, far away. He was no longer smiling, but frowning; his mind was turning back the years. For an endless moment he stood there in the patio as if alone, then started slowly walking. At the gate that led to the open area between house and corrals, two servant boys heard him murmur.

"A bridle . . . A halter . . . . With rosettes . . . . A horse to ride, of his own."

As the gate opened, he went through, strode on slowly down the slope, out past the corrals and into an open field. The two

---

*Indeed yes! So much so that Celia, by her own confessions forty years later, used that technique of tears every Sunday for weeks!

boys there never suspected they had heard not Francisco Villa murmuring, but a thirteen-year-old lad named Doroteo Arango.

It was Monday morning of the second week that Papa Pancho began his family's daily runs. He had felt restless energy welling again within him, and decided suddenly that he was "becoming soft like a gringo." Immediately after 6 o'clock breakfast that day he called all the children to him again.

"Hurry now," he ordered, "and put on strong shoes. We are going outside."

The youngsters protested. "Now? Now, Papa?"

"Now! Begone, and back here in five minutes."

The juvenile army obeyed, the servant women helping find and tie on the shoes. When all had met him again in the patio he was hatless and coatless, but he was smiling in anticipation. He opened the gate with a general's command, "Follow me."

Then he charged. Like a cavalry horse, the centaur charged; first a quick sprint, with a loud, happy "Whoop!" then a hearty trot. Twice he glanced back, smiling happily. The children were at his heels. He did not try to outrun them, instead he reached to take the two smallest by the hand and help them along. The sun itself had not stirred from its bed somewhere in Texas — he had told the children that the sun slept there — but its first rays were fanning over the horizon hills. When the little troupe topped a rise not far from the house, their forms were beautifully silhouetted and made an unforgettable picture.

Down the first grassy slope a little way he paused for all to get their breaths, then suddenly he squatted. He rubbed his hands on the clean, cold dew and washed his face with it.

"Why are you wetting yourself, papa?" one child demanded.

He laughed heartily and wet his face some more. "Because I have freckles."

It was a childish answer, for a child; but he himself knew he was communing. He was touching the physical universe, the soil for which he instinctively felt close kinship. It was almost ritualistic.

Curious youth of course pursued that. "Dew, Papa? For freckles?"

"It is a magic secret."

"It *is?*"

That enthralled them, he observed, smiling. They crowded

close, wide eyed. Sure enough the dark brown spots seemed to fade under the pink glow of his rubbings. If this was due to the rubbing itself rather than the dew, no matter. His smile grew bigger.

"We must come here often," said he. "Every morning. Dew is made in — in heaven." He studied them as if for corroboration. "Yes, in heaven."

Celia the pretty one, the spoiled one, the vain one, began to rub her own face.

"Ah ha, you would wash off yours with the magic secret!"

Together they brushed the wet grass and massaged her face, laughing together, and again he saw the color blush cause the freckles momentarily to subside. He felt as happy about it as did the children.

More and more he found himself enjoying the company of his children and their small friends. It was as if he had a special kinship with them, an understanding that he lacked with many adults. He would pause during play with them to consider his reactions. "It is their innocence," he decided, and murmured it to himself. "They trust everybody. A shame, they have to grow up."

Among his first orders issued at the rancho was one for erection of a school.

"Mexican children must be educated," he announced, rather pontifically on that occasion, because he had considerable adult audience. "I will start with my own. Ignorance is the first guarantee of poverty and peonage."

"But you had no schooling, patron," a friend suggested.

"Truly I did not. And who would know better the need for it?"

"You will have your children taught farming?"

"I will have them taught everything! Farming is for peons, but even peons can learn not to be slaves. Poor Mexicans and rich alike must be schooled. It is what I have fought for, eh? They must learn never again to accept slavery. They must learn the ideal of freedom, they must not be sheep!" He was actually trembling a little, in the intensity of his feeling.

With ceremony marked by his own display of emotion, he had named the new structure Felipe Angeles School, honoring his great friend of war years. He unveiled a bust of Felipe stationed at the entrance, and told newspaper men of Felipe's brilliance and valor.

So it was, then, that he found months of happiness-with-peace. Time and time again he shook his head in disbelief — this new state was incredible! Banditry? Warfare? Politics? Hah! He was now appalled at the life behind him. *This* was what God meant man to do, he kept telling himself.

.

22

ON THIS SUNKISSED MORNING in 1923 Pancho was astir even before his usual early hour. He had come to resent the necessity for sleep anyway; life had so much of interest, such constant lure. He especially enjoyed this time of pre-dawn planning. His mind then seemed youthful, sharp, clear, so he told himself. For one thing, he ate sparingly of breakfast and felt that such a regimen kept his mind alert.

"The bloods, she do not have to work in the estomach, *amigo*," he philosophized about it to an American friend. "She can go work in the brain, eh? Is good."

The American agreed. "Most people eat too much."

"*Si*. Me, I estuff my gut when I loos the battle. I get seek. Is fool. Is no more fool now."

This morning he had saddled a placid horse that could be guided by knee pressures; Pancho liked his hands to be as free as his mind. As he rode, he plucked off twigs, or leaves, or flowers if they were within reach. He found a dead dove, its brains neatly eaten out by a butcher bird, and swung down from his saddle to retrieve it. He plucked one long tail feather and stuck that in his hatband, humming and smiling at his moment of vanity. Then he forced his mind to work on details of a new irrigation project, for he was riding six miles to the area that seemed ideal for it. He started whistling, glad that he could ride as a free man should, studying the land and the sky.

As always, the sky especially interested him. Northern Mexico was arid, but majestic thunderstorms seemed always to lurk behind the horizon mountains as his own cavalry used to do, ready to rush out and attack the plains. Now if he could just control these water freshets as he had controlled his Dorados, conserving them for use when need was greatest — so ran his mind.

A mile from home he rode within sight of a peon's hut and there a child saw him and came rushing out. Pancho lifted the little girl to the saddle in front of him and rode her back to her house.

"Good morning, *señora*," he greeted the happy mother with a smile. He saw her smile in turn, and a new gold tooth shone — infallible sign of prosperity. "Where is Chucho this morning? Is the lazy good-for-nothing up yet?"

He knew that Chucho (familiar form of the popular name Jesus) was honored to have General Villa call him that. Chucho came out of the hut now, and was holding his jaw. He looked up in misery.

"A toothache," Pancho diagnosed. "A swelling. Well now, my friend, I carried tools in my saddle bags for twenty years to pull the teeth of the soldiers. I can do no less for you. Stand close here and open your mouth."

They were pliers from a new Dodge automobile acquired by Rancho Cañutillo, and while they had some car grease on them, they served well. From his saddle Pancho managed to get a good "bite" on the tooth, then yanked. He all but lifted Chucho off his feet. That worthy yelped and danced around like a stuck pig, not without cause; the molar tossed as a souvenir to the little girl was "big enough for a horse," said Pancho.

A boy of ten or eleven had run out to witness the operation, and Pancho called to him. "You look like something from the Yaqui Indians, only not so handsome," the big man ruled. "*Señora*, have you no scissors?"

"No sir," the mother replied.

"Then get some. At the ranch house. Say that I ordered it. Boy, climb here astride my horse's neck and sit still."

From the same saddle bag came shears, and in five minutes Chucho's young son lost five years of hair.

"I have not enough time for this," Pancho ruled, studying the grinning lad. "Chucho, you learn to use pliers and scissors. I appoint you dentist and barber of the ranch. Get an outfit and ride to all the homes and take care of the people's needs. I will not have my people looking like shaggy animals." Pancho knew that Chucho was honored; would have new stature in the ranch social life.

He enjoyed these homely little incidents more than he had ever imagined. "Maybe I am just getting old," he confessed wryly to a friend one day, telling of his new life.

He found time to do some wild game hunting; quail, doves, deer, pumas, bobcats, all fell before his unerring aim. One week he quite outdid himself. He rode out alone and came home with a 116-pound panther, very much alive and snarling. He had tracked it with dogs, treed it, roped it on a limb, pushed it off the limb to hang it by the neck. Then with shorter ropes (the "piggin strings" of American cowboys) he had tied the beast's legs together and put a long sapling pole between them, trussing him tightly there. One end of the pole on his saddle and the other end dragging had made it an effective Indian travois.

The incident made news all over the ranch, he discovered happily; made Pancho *mucho hombre* — much man — all over again. He hung the lion skin, duly tanned, as a trophy in his home. He loved to spread it on the floor of the patio in the sunshine and call his children to him for a romp on it. Once he put son Augustin under the rug to give it life, put Celia on his shoulders and himself played horse, while they reenacted the scene of the lion chase and capture.

All of this while, too, he was developing the ranch village. Houses were built for farmers and employees. Streets were laid out with a post office, masonry shop, carpentry shop, butcher, shoe man, grocer, clothier. Pancho was director of all these enterprises.

Newspaper feature writers from everywhere swarmed down to the vast Rancho Cañutillo, and because he was hospitable they often overstayed their welcome. Yet it was from them that he got the first hints of doom.

"I wouldn't put too much trust in General Martinez, sir," one astute correspondent suggested. "I spent some time with him. I think the man is spying on you. He knows too much of your intimate doings here."

Pancho was furious, but he checked up on the warning and found it justified. His own friends in high places learned that Eugenio Martinez, he who had signed the pact of truce, was being paid 4,000 pesos a month by the government just to watch Francisco Villa.

"Why are they haunting me?" he cried out. "I am living up to my side of the bargain. Who is afraid of me, and why? I ask only to be let alone."

Down in Mexico City, Pancho learned, Obregon had acquired the presidency but it was an unstable job, and he hoped to shunt it to his friend Calles. Friends of Adolfo de la Huerta were threatening rebellion, and both sides feared what the always dangerous Villa might do. Both knew that he was still in his middle forties, very capable of materializing another army out of the hills. He frowned at this report, worrying. His bright new horizon had suddenly clouded.

To get at the truth, Pancho sent his trusted friend Miguel Trillo to Mexico City to ask President Obregon for a renewal of his personal guarantee. Trillo got it. Obregon even agreed to lend Villa 100,000 pesos for farm development, saying the government wanted to encourage his ranch activity every way.

This report and loan reassured Pancho and he plunged into work with more energy than ever. Two American mining engineers came into the region and asked to see him. They had not expected the hospitality he showed them, they said, and were astonished at his progressive, modern enterprises. Pancho was flattered. Having some mining interests of his own, he even accompanied the two men as guide, showing them the Sierra where he had ridden. Later, back in America, these two men told in magazines that Pancho Villa the Mexican Cincinnatus was the soul of courtesy and kindness, and that as a civilian he was now leading the reforms he had always advocated. Copies of their report reached him, and he was mightily pleased. He felt that progress was being made again toward a better understanding with the United States. He even suggested that the time had come for improving the immigration laws of both nations, in a new treaty of friendship. He had virtually forgotten the warning; he was singing and whistling again.

Then one day early in June of 1923 he was asked to come to the town of Rio Florido to be godfather of a friend's child. A few hours before he was to go, a woman of his village asked if she might talk with him.

"General Villa," she whispered it, when given permission, "there is a plot to murder you."

He grabbed her arm. "Don't speak gossip, woman! Why do you say this? Where have you heard it?"

"It is in the air, General. I have also read it in the ashes. I can feel it in my very bones."

A female soothsayer, then. An old crone, bent on melodramatics. He tried to shrug it off. Yet she was disturbing. The anguish of worry came back to him strong. He had left too many enemies behind him over the years, and it was entirely possible that some of them still craved revenge no matter how he himself may have changed. The weird old woman with her witchlike way of talking might indeed have heard some clandestine plans. He well knew the strange word-of-mouth way that news traveled in Mexico. It was like the Indians' "grapevine" — nobody told a thing, yet everybody knew it. And most of his peons themselves were of Indian blood.

That same week a child in the village died, and when the funeral procession started to the cemetery, the coffin on the father's shoulder, Pancho was watching respectfully at a corner of the village street. Someone came close and touched his arm. He turned to behold that same old woman. She had a haunted look, a witch look indeed, and she pointed a bony finger at the coffin then back at him.

"Guard yourself, my general," she whispered her warning anew. "Beware for your own life. They will try to kill you *soon*."

It was fantastic, he told himself, but it was not to be ignored. It would have passed as a childrens' ghost story in any normal surroundings, the old woman becoming a character to be treated kindly because obviously her mind had failed. Pancho tried to dismiss her on that basis, but in the same hour he strapped a pistol on. He told his household that coyotes and snakes had been seen and he might have to kill a few. He spoke figuratively, with far deeper meaning than they suspected. They got their first hint of his worry on July 17, the day before he was to go to the christening.

"I shall stop in Parral long enough to have a lawyer draw up details of my will," said he to his wife Austreberta.

"Your will?" she was surprised. "You are only forty-five years old. Are you planning to die so soon?"

"Nobody plans to die, woman. But a smart man plans for his family if he should die."

That night the sensitivity was transmitted to his children. He was taking them to bed, as usual. He loved this nightly ritual in the home; he would tell stories and maybe romp a little, then outline plans for the morrow. Sometimes he would play horse and carry them to bedrooms on his shoulders. But this night he sat in a chair and gathered all the nightie-clad youngsters close. He was not smiling, he had no spirit of fun in his heart.

"I have to go on a trip soon," he told them gently. "And I may not come back. I want to hug you tonight."

"What do you mean, father?" one spoke the concern for all.

"You are not to worry. Just let me say one thing — if we don't see each other again in this life, children, we'll see each other in the next."

A strange thing to say to children, he told himself later. But he had received premonition, more than an old soothsayer's whispered warning. His own close associates had heard the rumors of plotting against him and he was doubly warned. He tried to dispel anxiety, and could not.

Colonel Trillo, his close friend, vetoed the plan to ride horseback into Rio Florido for the christening. The ranch had a good Dodge touring car, said he; Pancho must go in that, with an escort, it will be much faster and less likely to be ambushed.

He accepted the change, and with Colonel Trillo and two other armed men did motor in. It was an uneventful ride. The baby was duly christened with Pancho as its godfather, the gifts presented, the happy words and greetings all said. Then Pancho with his three companions on their return trip went by way of Parral. In this larger town they could pick up some needed ranch supplies. This and other business, including a visit to his lawyer, would take maybe two days, he had told his family. He kept up a hearty front.

Strangely enough, the same old woman who had already warned him of danger turned up also in Parral and once more sought an audience with him. When he identified her he received her at once. She spoke only as she had spoken before — in vague terms, but with a sense of greater urgency now. Pancho hardly knew what to make of it. Actually, what *could* he do about it, he asked himself. An ex-General, a bold bandit, a fearless leader of men, can't go cringing up the hedgerows just because some half-witted, witchlike old woman insisted on scaring him. The matter touched his pride so that he became angry with her and ordered her away, though he did give her some money this time. He tried to dismiss her from his thoughts by laughing at her with his lawyer. The lawyer laughed too. "We get some strange ones among our peons, *no es verdad*, General?" said he.

He took time in Parral to attend to something that actually was more to his liking than making a will. He visited a woman, hoping thus to ease his fears. This was no ordinary woman, nor yet a stranger. Her name was Manuela Casas de Villa, and she had the honor of being one of General Pancho Villa's ex-wives. Quite a few women had that honor, yet most of them held no interest for him now, which fact set Manuela apart. Because he and Austreberta were not wholly compatible, he had quietly slipped back to Manuela several times of late. Thus did he return to one wife while actually being married to and living with another just thirty miles away.

Manuela's home was near the corner of Juarez Avenue and Gabine Barreda street in Parral, about one hundred yards from a little bridge there in the outskirts of town. Not many houses were in this area, hence it had been easy for him to go there unseen. His visit to her on this trip was satisfactory, and he left her to go back downtown early on July 20, 1923. There he picked up his three companions in the Dodge automobile and started the return trip to Cañutillo. Pancho himself was driving.

Toward the end of Juarez Avenue they heard a fruit vendor there appear to salute them. "VIVA VILLA!" the man yelled from his little cart. Those in the car never knew it was a prearranged signal.

Pancho smiled and lifted his hand in acknowledgment. At the same moment he turned the car onto Gabine Barreda Street. He slowed to cross the little bridge. Manuela's house seemed lonely when he glanced once at it in farewell, sitting in the background. Another, more barnlike structure was near the bridge. It held no interest. Bright sunshine bathed them or winked through the scattered trees, and the travelers were intent on getting home again. The Dodge bumped over the wooden bridge and Pancho was beginning to accelerate it again when some men came running from that farmlike building.

All at once the air was ripped by streaks of flame. The sharp crack of pistols was heard, then the awesome *tat-tat-tat-tat-tat* of a machine gun, a sound as terrorizing as that of a rattlesnake's whirr.

Pancho tried to stand, clawing at his pistol in its holster. He had let go of the steering wheel, so the car whirled then crashed into a tree. *Tat-tat-tat-tat-tat-tat.* One of the men in the back seat, Ramon Contreras, leaped out with his arms folded low. His intestines were flowing over them as if he had been slashed with a knife. Another, named Carlitos, ran a few steps, knelt in agony, then toppled over dead.

Tat-tat-tat-tat-tat-tat.

The bursts came with only short pauses between them, the car body began to look like a sieve. Screams of men were horrifying, because other men were shooting with deliberate, vengeful aim. Colonel Trillo's body was bent backward so as to hang face out over the right front door, the skin already purpling. (There is a shocking, documentary photograph of him hanging so, made by some alert citizen who had presence of mind to grab a camera when he heard the shooting.)

And what now of General Francisco Villa the Chihuahuan centaur, the Tiger of the North, the gentleman farmer?

That first volley probably killed him. He slumped, twisted over the steering wheel. Then his assailants came closer, so as to work with methodical care. *Bang . . . Bang . . . Tat-tat-tat-tat.* They pumped shot after shot into him, working fiendishly. The face and chest were peppered and the blood gushed. Later it was found that one projectile had exploded literally in his heart. After that at least forty bullets, most of them the type then in use by the federal army, had torn through Mexico's man of the century.

THE END